THE CHEMISTRY OF MOLTEN SALTS

THE PHYSICAL INORGANIC CHEMISTRY SERIES

Robert A. Plane and Michell J. Sienko, Editors

Oxygen: Elementary Forms and Hydrogen Peroxide — *M. Ardon (Hebrew University of Jerusalem)*

The Chemistry of Molten Salts — *H. Bloom (University of Tasmania)*

Inorganic Reaction Mechanisms — *J. O. Edwards (Brown)*

Metal Ions in Aqueous Solution — *J. P. Hunt (Washington State)*

Inorganic Chemistry of Nitrogen — *W. L. Jolly (Berkeley)*

The Solid-State Chemistry of Binary Metal Hydrides — *G. G. Libowitz (Kennecott Copper)*

Boron Hydrides — *W. N. Lipscomb (Harvard)*

Elements of Inorganic Chemistry — *R. A. Plane and R. E. Hester (Cornell)*

Periodic Correlations — *R. L. Rich (Bethel College)*

Physical Inorganic Chemistry — *M. J. Sienko and R. A. Plane (Cornell)*

THE CHEMISTRY
OF MOLTEN SALTS

*An Introduction to the Physical and Inorganic
Chemistry of Molten Salts and Salt Vapors*

HARRY BLOOM

University of Tasmania

W. A. BENJAMIN, INC.

1967   New York   Amsterdam

THE CHEMISTRY OF MOLTEN SALTS

Library of Congress Catalog Card Number 67-27151
Manufactured in the United States of America

*The manuscript was put into production on January 24, 1967;
this volume was published on September 17, 1967*

W. A. BENJAMIN, INC.
NEW YORK, NEW YORK 10016

TO NORMA

Editors' Foreword

In recent years few fields of chemistry have expanded at a rate to match that of inorganic chemistry. Aside from the stimulus afforded by the demand for new materials, a primary cause for the resurgence has been the application of physics and physical chemistry concepts to inorganic problems. As a result, both researchers active in the field and students entering the field need to become as thoroughly familiar with physical concepts as with descriptive information. However, there is presently no single point of view sufficiently general to organize the entire discipline. Instead, various points of view have arisen corresponding to the most powerful methods of attack in each research area. The synthesis of these different points of view constitutes the present series of monographs.

The series in total is a reference treatise on inorganic chemistry systematized by physical principles. Each monograph is contributed by an inorganic chemist active in a particular research area and reflects the methods of approach characteristic of that area. Our operational procedure has been to invite able scientists to write where their interests lead them. The aim is for a specialist's introduction to a current research field.

It is hoped that the authors contributing to this series have succeeded in directing attention to unsolved problems and that their efforts will be repaid by continued research advances in inorganic chemistry. Professor Bloom's outstanding research in molten salt chemistry makes his monograph a valuable contribution to the series.

M. J. Sienko
R. A. Plane

Ithaca, New York
July 1967

Preface

The development of chemistry to date has been largely shaped by the use of water and other room temperature liquids as solvents. Modern electrochemistry has followed, to a large extent, the lines opened up by the outstanding success of the Debye-Hückel theory of dilute solutions with extensions by Fuoss and others into more concentrated solutions. The chemistry of pure ionic liquids, that is, molten salts, oxides, and so on, and the vapor and solid phases in equilibrium with this class of liquids, has mostly been overlooked in courses of instruction, with the result that the average college graduate has had little or no acquaintance with this vast and industrially important field.

This book is designed as an introductory text in molten salt chemistry, particularly for students of physical chemistry, electrochemistry, and allied topics. A knowledge of elementary mathematics and physical chemistry (particularly thermodynamics) is assumed. Examples are selected to illustrate various principles.

Throughout, the discussion relies on the presentation of simple models rather than on a complex mathematical treatment, and by an application of the principles presented, the student who completes the course should have a better insight into the workings of high temperature electrochemical processes, chemical reactions involving high temperature liquids and vapors, and likely future extensions of these processes and reactions. The application of simple thermodynamics to the largely nonideal liquid and vapor mixtures formed in this class of substances will be a useful extension to usual courses in thermodynamics.

The material covered in this text may be used in conjunction with many different courses, including those dealing with the thermodynamics of liquids, electrochemistry, inorganic preparative chemistry, phase rule studies, and the thermodynamics of vapors.

Finally, the author acknowledges with gratitude the assistance of Miss Margaret Smith in typing the manuscript, of Mr. E. L. Valentine for the preparation of the diagrams, and of Dr. John D. Corbett, Dr. Michell J. Sienko, Dr. J. W. Hastie, Fr. V. C. Reinsborough, and Mr. I. Weeks for their helpful comments.

H. Bloom

Hobart, Tasmania
June 1967

Contents

THE CHEMISTRY OF MOLTEN SALTS

1

Introduction

Many references to chemical reactions at high temperature have been recorded in the literature from the earliest of times. These include combustion, the smelting of metals such as copper and iron, and the production of glass. The electrolysis of alumina dissolved in molten cryolite for the electrowinning of aluminum is a more recent example of the commercial importance of high temperature chemistry. Sodium, magnesium, the alkaline earth metals, and other commercially important elements rely also on the use of high temperature methods for their production. Many of the main metallurgical industries utilize chemical processes at high temperature. With the imminence of extraterrestrial travel, high temperature chemistry has assumed a new importance because of the practical need for processes to provide propulsion as in rocket engines.

One main interest in high temperature chemistry at present is directed toward the economical production of the less common metals, including titanium, zirconium, thorium, beryllium, niobium, and tantalum, which are potentially suitable for use in jet engines, rockets, space vehicles, and high temperature nuclear reactors. The use of high temperature systems involving either solid or liquid fuels would be advantageous for use in nuclear reactors to produce electric power. Fuel cells using molten carbonate

1

electrolytes and cheap carbonaceous fuels such as natural gas, petroleum, and coke may well prove feasible on an economic scale. Another potential source of electric power is the molten salt thermocell, in which pairs of electrodes reversible to a molten salt, for example, silver electrodes in molten silver nitrate, are subjected to a thermal gradient, thus producing electricity with low internal resistance. In this application the electrodes are not ultimately consumed, as silver that goes into solution at one electrode is deposited at the other. A conventional source of heat, such as the burning of natural gas, could be used to produce the thermal gradient.

High temperature chemistry can be divided conveniently into three main classifications: (1) reactions of molten metals, salts, and oxides; (2) reactions involving gas or vapor systems; and (3) solid state reactions. Subdivision is further possible on an arbitrary basis according to the relevant temperature range—for example, reactions below 1000°C and those above. Most of the chemistry dealt with in this volume will be in the lower temperature range, as precise measurements above 1000°C, except in the field of spectroscopy, are not numerous.

Chemistry at very high temperature can be a good deal more complex than at room temperature owing to unusual oxidation numbers of elements and formulas of compounds. Instead of the familiar oxidation numbers, 1 for alkali metals, 2 for alkaline earth metals, and so on, other values are more familiar in high temperature vapors; for example, LiO is stable at high temperatures and molecules with barium in both 1 and 3 oxidation states are observed. Aluminum occurs in both 1 and 2 oxidation states, while its low temperature state 3 is not at all common. The complexity of gaseous systems can also increase with increase of temperature due to change in the number of atoms per molecule from the familiar 2 or 3 at low temperatures to as many as 5, 10, and more. For example, in the equilibrium between gaseous and solid boron sulfide, molecules with twenty, thirty, or more atoms are observed. A knowledge of gaseous equilibria at high temperature is of fundamental importance in the study of the chemistry in the atmospheres of the sun and stars and in plasmas.

In a book of this scope it would be impossible to cover all aspects of high temperature chemistry; hence, metallurgical chemistry and solid state reactions, which cover major fields in themselves, will receive little attention. Topics to be dealt with in greater detail will include molten salts and gaseous systems in equilibrium with molten salts.

1-1 MOLTEN SALTS

The development of conventional chemistry has hitherto been influenced very strongly by the abundance of water as a solvent. Thus the evolution of many chemical manufacturing processes has been controlled by this view and further investigations have been directed to improving these processes rather than to the discovery from first principles of better ones.   This has impeded progress in many preparative chemical industries.

In actual fact molten salts are often much better and more versatile solvents than water and other room temperature liquids, being capable of dissolving such diverse substances as water, organic substances, metals, oxides, other salts, and nonmetallic elements.   In molten salts the solvent properties and the effect of these solvents on chemical reactions are affected, among other factors, by the wide variety of solvent temperatures available, from the eutectic mixture of $AlCl_3$ + $NaCl$ + KCl (m.p. 89°C) to high melting salts such as cryolite (Na_3AlF_6, m.p. 1003°C).   Different molten salt systems give rise to media of vastly different oxidizing properties, ranging from strong oxidizing to strong reducing systems, and different acidities, including basic molten Na_2S and acidic molten $ZnCl_2$.   This greatly influences the course of chemical reactions, which may proceed in different ways in different molten salt solvents.

For carrying out chemical reactions, molten salt systems possess a number of other advantages; for example, in molten salt systems, the range of stability in oxidation-reduction systems is much greater than in aqueous solution, where the relatively small decomposition potential (1.2 volts) of water provides a limitation.   In the LiCl + KCl eutectic at 700°C the range of stability is about 3.5 volts and in the CsCl + MgCl₂ eutectic about 2.6 volts at the same temperature.   Thus highly electropositive metals can be obtained by electrolysis in molten salt solutions in the absence of water. Moreover, the higher temperature of molten salt solvents causes a very marked increase of reaction rate, leading to reaction times of only a few seconds for both organic and inorganic reactions.   This factor, coupled with the very high yields achieved (often approaching 100%), makes molten salts ideal solvents for a large variety of chemical reactions.   Investigations proceeding along these lines will have the effect of greatly changing many common chemical manufacturing processes.

1-2   THE PHYSICAL PROPERTIES OF MOLTEN SALTS

For molten salts, the physical properties can be divided into (a) nonelectrolyte and (b) electrolyte properties.

Molten salts have nonelectrolyte properties similar in magnitude to those of room temperature liquids, in spite of the obvious temperature differences.   Thus the molten alkali halides are clear waterlike liquids that have comparable refractive index, viscosity, surface tension, and only a slightly higher thermal conductivity than water itself.   The vast difference in cohesive forces between the two classes of liquids is thus compensated to a large extent by the different temperature ranges of existence.

The different types of cohesive forces for the two classes of liquids do, however, lead to very different temperature ranges of stability. Thus molten sodium chloride with its strong electrical forces between Na^+ and Cl^- at approximately close-packed distances has a normal liquid range of about 600°C, compared with 100° for water with its weaker dipolar forces (hydrogen bonding).

As far as electrical conductance is concerned, molten salts have values that are far in excess of those for room temperature liquids. Thus molten NaCl has a specific conductance that is some 10^8 times as great as that of water, although it is still much less than that of a typical well-conducting metal such as copper or molten sodium. Molten salts are in fact by far the best class of ionic conductors; for example, molten KCl at 800°C has a specific conductance about 22 times that of normal aqueous KCl solution at 20°C, while equivalent conductance of molten lithium chloride is 180.8 ohm^{-1} cm^2 at 710°C compared with 115.0 ohm^{-1} cm^2 for its aqueous solution at 25°C and at infinite dilution. The adherence to Faraday's laws indicates that the process of conduction is ionic, but although such a liquid is largely constituted of ions in close proximity, it will be shown in later chapters that small tightly bound groupings such as ion pairs and complex ions can be present.

1-3   SALT VAPORS

Investigation of the chemistry of salt vapors is even more recent than that of molten salts. It was reported by Nernst in 1903 that the molecular weights of vapors of the alkali chlorides were the simple formula weights of these compounds; hence they were assumed to exist as simple molecules or perhaps ion pairs. Since about 1950, however, various investigators have found, using a variety of methods, that saturated vapors above molten salts and their mixtures consist in many cases largely of polymeric species. In some vapors, the monomeric ion pair may be present only in the minority, and in lithium chloride vapor, $(LiCl)_2$, $(LiCl)_3$, and $(LiCl)_4$ predominate, the simple monomer LiCl being present only in small proportions. The complexity and proportions of the various polymeric species depend on temperature and pressure. Above mixtures of molten salts intermolecular compounds exist; for example, $KCdCl_3$ occurs above mixtures of KCl and $CdCl_2$.

1-4   METHODS OF INVESTIGATION OF MOLTEN SALTS

Earliest investigations consisted mainly of determination of the melting point; for example, in 1888 Hautefeuille and Perry recorded melting points for a number of silicates.   Even as early as 1897, Moissan used arc furnaces for high temperature preparations and in 1905 described the volatilization of graphite at temperatures in excess of 3000°C.

Systematic thermodynamic and kinetic studies at temperatures below 1000°C commenced in the early 1900's, and those for temperatures above 1000°C began later than 1930.   Until fairly recently there was a lack of much fundamental work on such essentials as the accurate determination of temperature, particularly above 1100°C.

The lack of convenient refractory materials often leads to experimental difficulty in high temperature chemistry.   Molten salts and vapors are often extremely corrosive and their solvent properties depend on composition and temperature, fluorides being particularly corrosive.   Accurate measurement of physical properties depends to a large extent on the choice of the refractory container material but even "inert" metals such as platinum are soluble to a greater or lesser degree in molten salt solvents.

Many investigations of the physical properties of molten salts have been carried out for different purposes.   Structural information can be obtained most readily from investigation of properties such as X-ray and neutron diffraction, molar volume, electrical conductance, molar refractivity, absorption spectroscopy, sound velocity, and viscosity.   Thermodynamic information from measurement of emf of formation cells, vapor pressure, cryoscopy, heat of mixing, and so on, can be used to test models for molten salts and their mixtures, and thus also contribute information on structure.   For practical purposes it is necessary to determine melting point, solubility, vapor pressure, viscosity, and electrolytic conductances as well as other properties.   For extracting metals electrolytically, a knowledge of the electrode kinetics in molten salt solvents is also desirable.   In subsequent chapters these properties will be discussed and the type of information deduced from them will be indicated.

SUGGESTED READING

1. *Physico-chemical Measurements at High Temperatures*, J. O'M. Bockris, J. L. White, and J. D. Mackenzie, eds., Butterworths, London, 1959.
2. Recent progress in the high temperature chemistry of Inorganic Salt Systems, H. Bloom, *Pure and Applied Chem.*, **7**, 389 (1963).
3. Structure and properties of molten salts, E. A. Ukshe, *Russian Chem. Rev.* (English trans.), **34, 141** (1965).

2

The Structure of Molten Salts with Special Reference to Halides

Structural conclusions on liquids in general are always more speculative than for solids or gases. For molten salts the experimental difficulties associated with physical measurements further aggravate the situation. In these systems structural inferences have been made by a variety of means. Direct methods such as X-ray and neutron diffraction give information on average interionic distances and coordination numbers. From the combined results of measurements of other physical properties, such as density, conductivity, spectra, and so on, structural models can be proposed and tested.

2-1 THE CONSTITUENT ENTITIES OF MOLTEN HALIDES

A typical crystalline salt, such as sodium chloride, can be shown by X-ray diffraction and other studies to consist of ions packed in a three-dimensional lattice. The NaCl lattice is face centered cubic, the ions being close packed with coordination number 6. Other typically ionic salts can be classified into various crystal symmetry systems, which include the fluorite

6

(CaF$_2$) and zinc blende (ZnS) structures. The crystal structure of sodium chloride is shown in Fig. 2-1.

Apart from salts that have typically ionic lattices, many are partly covalent and crystallize in layer structures; an example is CdCl$_2$, in which the octahedral CdCl$_6^{4-}$ groups are linked to form infinite layers as in Fig. 2-2. In cadmium chloride, the chloride ions are arranged in a cubic close-packed structure, two layers being fitted together with atoms of the one layer (e.g., the upper shaded circles in Fig. 2-2) falling above the hollows of the lower

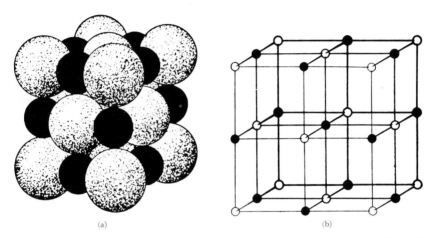

(a)   (b)

Fig. 2-1. *The arrangement of Na$^+$ (black spheres) and Cl$^-$ in the sodium chloride crystal: (a) crystal structure (to scale); (b) the lattice.*

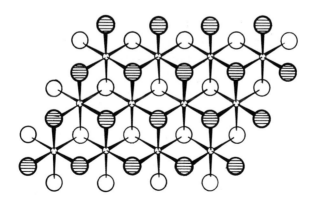

Fig. 2-2. *Composite layer of composition CdCl$_2$ consisting of two layers of Cl$^-$ with a layer of Cd^{2+} (small circles) in octahedral holes (between chloride layers).*

layer (unshaded). The small circles represent Cd^{2+} ions in a plane midway between the two chloride layers and mark the centers of octahedral holes. In $CdCl_2$ the Cd^{2+} occupy half the total available octahedral holes and the two adjacent layers of Cl^- with Cd^{2+} between them form a composite Cl–Cd–Cl layer. This packing is illustrated by a model of part of the structure in Fig. 2-3. To emphasize the layer structure of $CdCl_2$, the octahedra (with $6Cl^-$ at the corners and the Cd^{2+} at the centers) are shown as units sharing three edges with neighboring octahedra in Fig. 2-4. These infinite layers are held together by van der Waals forces. Other crystals that have layer structures include $CrCl_3$ (cubic packing) and CdI_2 (hexagonal packing).

Melting may be regarded as a process that frees the individual structural units of the crystal from the rigid confines of the lattice and allows their individual movement. Michael Faraday in the 1830's was the first to make a systematic study of electrochemical properties of molten salts, for which he established a series of comparative electromotive force and verified the application of the laws of electrolysis that bear his name. Molten salts are thus

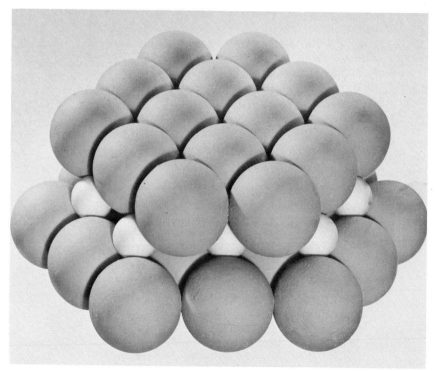

Fig. 2-3. *CdCl₂ structure (smaller spheres represent Cd²⁺).*

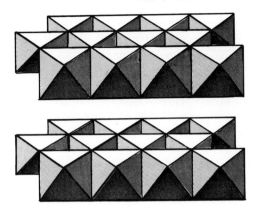

Fig. 2-4. *Part of the layer lattice of CdCl₂.* (*Each octahedron represents* $CdCl_6^{4-}$.)

liquids having as structural units ions that have considerable freedom of movement under the influence of an electric field, leading therefore to very high electrical conductances. They have for this reason often been termed *molten electrolytes*, *liquid electrolytes*, or *ionic liquids*. Although they can be regarded as consisting mainly of "free" ions, the powerful forces of attraction between oppositely charged species impose restrictions on the movement of these particles. Many molten salts also have as structural units associated groups such as *ion pairs* or *complex ions*.

When a crystalline salt melts, the ions formerly fixed in the rigid lattice not only become free to move but adopt, on the average, modified interparticle distances. Experimentally, it is found that most salts melt with considerable increase of volume and that the well-defined X-ray diffraction pattern of the solid becomes diffuse. For the alkali halides, melting causes an expansion of the order of 20%. Some results are shown in Table 2-1 (mainly from Ubbelohde [1]).

Table 2-1 *Percentage Volume Increase* $(100 \, \Delta V/V_s)$ *on Melting for Alkali Metal Halides*

	F	Cl	Br	I
Li	29.4	26.2	24.3	—
Na	27.4	25.0	22.4	18.6
K	17.2	17.3	16.6	15.9
Rb	—	14.3	13.5	—
Cs	—	10.5	26.8	28.5

In contrast to the melting characteristics of most close-packed crystalline salts, the volume change is much smaller for metals (e.g., 4.7% increase for Cd). Some even contract (e.g., Bi).

A volume expansion on melting is the general pattern for salts (with a few exceptions—e.g., ThF_4 and $RbNO_3$ contract slightly). This expansion explains why melts of close-packed salts are able to conduct electrolytically and flow as liquids since, apart from removing the restrictions of the crystal lattice, melting introduces empty space into the structure, making room into which ions can migrate. The empty space is known as *free volume* and can be present in two main ways: (a) *fluctuation volume*, which is the volume through which an ion can move in the "cage" formed by its neighbors, and (b) *hole volume*, which is the amount of empty space in the liquid present as individual units or *holes* that are on the average large enough to accommodate at least one of the ions.

X-ray diffraction studies (Lark-Horowitz and Miller,[2] Zarzycki,[3] Levy et al.[4]) will be interpreted in Section 2-2 to show that holes account for much of the free volume introduced into a salt on melting.

2-2   X-RAY AND NEUTRON DIFFRACTION STUDIES ON MOLTEN SALTS

Liquids do not have the simplifying features of either gases, which can be regarded in the first approximation as consisting of individual particles able to move independently of their neighbors, or solids, which can be treated theoretically as coupled oscillators whose mean positions are fixed in space. Theoretical methods of interpretation are therefore much more difficult with molten salts than with solids or gases as, in keeping with other liquids, molten salts have characteristics of both solids and gases. They have, moreover, the added complication of being composed of charged particles to which electrical restrictions also apply. Much useful information on this state of matter can, however, be gained from investigation of X-ray diffraction.

For solid powders, X-ray diffraction patterns have well-defined lines (arcs of circles), the spacings of which are related to the wavelength of the scattering radiation and distance apart of the ionic planes causing diffraction, by the Bragg equation. The absence of well-defined diffraction patterns makes such investigations infeasible for liquids. Instead, X-ray or neutron diffraction studies furnish information in the form of *pair radial distribution functions* (RDF), which give the probability that pairs of atoms are to be found separated by a given distance.

From the RDF, the average distance between like ions (i.e., cation–cation or anion–anion distance) and the average distance between unlike ions, as well as the average number of nearest neighbors (unlike ions) and second-nearest neighbors (like ions), can be determined.   Some RDF information from the work of Levy *et al.* is shown in Fig. 2-5.   The average number of neighbors is computed from areas under the various peaks, the positions of the peaks giving average separation in each case.   The first peak always refers to separation of ions of opposite charge and the second to ions of like charge.   Although the distinction between cation–cation and anion–anion separations cannot easily be determined from RDF information, Levy *et al.* have been able to obtain such information by careful analyses of the results of both X-ray and neutron diffraction for some salts using different isotopes.   The dotted line on the RDF diagram represents background scattering, which rises sharply with increase of distance from the reference ion.   The information on interionic distance and coordination number from RDF does not necessarily represent actual values—only averages over a long interval of time.   The standard synthetic peaks shown below the main solid curves in Fig. 2-5 correspond to Gaussian distribution of atomic pairs to yield the number of neighbors indicated in the figure.

A summary of average interionic distances and coordination numbers for several molten and solid salts is given in Table 2-2 (from X-ray diffraction results of Levy *et al.*).

RDF data show that, for the alkali halides: (a) average distance between unlike ions is significantly less in the melt than in the solid at the melting point; (b) average distance between like ions is greater in the melt; (c) average cation–anion coordination number is less in the melt than in the solid; and (d) there is a high degree of short-range order in the melt (well-defined first RDF peak), but the long-range order typical of the solid has been destroyed on melting.

Table 2-2   *Interionic Distance and Coordination Number for Some Molten and Solid Salts*

Salt	Liquid at m.p.			Solid at m.p.		
	Cation–anion distance ($\mathring{A}$)	Coordination number (cation–anion)	Cation–cation or anion–anion distance ($\mathring{A}$)	Cation–anion distance ($\mathring{A}$)	Coordination number (cation–anion)	Cation–cation or anion–anion distance ($\mathring{A}$)
LiCl	2.47	4.0	3.85	2.66	6	3.76
CsCl	3.53	4.6	4.87	3.57	6	5.05
LiI	2.85	5.6	4.45	3.12	6	4.41
NaI	3.15	4.0	4.80	3.35	6	4.74

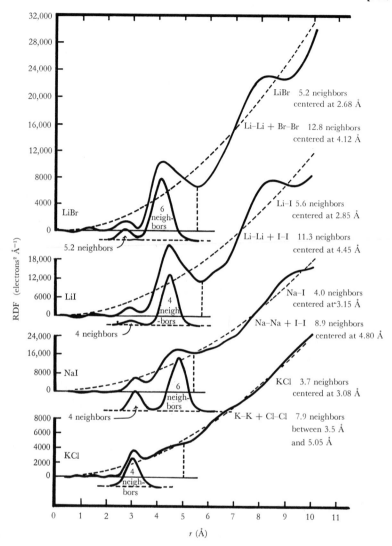

Fig. 2-5. *Radial distribution functions for molten LiBr, LiI, NaI, and KCl by X-ray diffraction, showing standard synthetic peaks and boundaries by which coordination numbers were obtained (from Levy et al.[4]).*

If, in conjunction with the RDF information, note is taken of the increase in volume on melting, an average physical picture of a molten alkali halide can be built up by starting with the solid, bringing the unlike ions closer, spreading out the like ions, and incorporating holes in the structure to accommodate the extra volume. At the same time the long-range order must be destroyed. The melting process is shown diagrammatically for NaCl in Figs. 2-6 and 2-7. Figure 2-6 is a two-dimensional representation of the NaCl structure. In Fig. 2-7 some 20% of the ions have been removed and the others spread about in the same area according to the deductions from RDF data. The presence of short-range order, lack of long-range order, and presence of holes are immediately apparent.

Fig. 2-6. *Two-dimensional representation of the NaCl structure. (Smaller circles represent Na⁺, larger circles represent Cl⁻.)*

Fig. 2-7. *Two-dimensional representation of NaCl melt.*

2-3 STRUCTURAL INFORMATION FROM OTHER PHYSICAL MEASUREMENTS

Another physical property that relates to distribution of ions in the melt is molar refractivity R, which can be calculated (in cubic centimeters) from refractive index n as follows.

$$R = \frac{n^2 - 1}{n^2 + 2} \cdot \frac{M}{d} \tag{2-1}$$

where M = molecular weight and d = density.

Measurements of refractive index will be discussed in Chapter 6. Refractivity values using sodium illumination for several molten salts are given in Table 2-3, together with the values for the solid at room temperature, the infinitely dilute aqueous solution at 25°C, and the *gaseous ions* (i.e., the theoretical value of R calculated for the ions at such a wide separation as to have no influence on each other).

The molar refractivity values for molten salts are higher than for the solid and are generally higher even than in states of dispersion in which all interactions have been eliminated (i.e., infinitely dilute solution and gaseous ions); R, however, increases slightly with increase of temperature (up to 0.002 cm³ per degree) and when the results for molten salts are adjusted for their higher temperature, they become comparable with those at infinite dilution, indicating that the ionic atmospheres in molten salts are on the average symmetrical, as in infinitely dilute solution.

The transmission of ultrasonic vibrations and heat through molten salts also gives information of their structure. Bockris and Richards [6] applied the ultrasonic velocity data to calculation of free volume in molten salts, using for calculation of free volume per mole V_f the equation

$$V_f = \left[\frac{1}{U_L} \left(\frac{RT}{2(M_c M_a)^{1/2}} \right)^{1/2} \right]^3 V \qquad (2\text{-}2)$$

where U_L is velocity of ultrasonic vibrations in the liquid, R the gas constant, V the molar volume, and M_c, M_a the mass of cation and anion, respectively.

Free volume from Eq. (2-2) and measured ultrasonic velocities gave values that were only about 15% of the volume increase on melting. This was explained as follows. When ultrasonic vibrations of frequency 10^6 cycles sec^{-1} are superimposed upon the normal (10^{13} cycles sec^{-1}) vibrations of ions in the melt, the forced vibrations are transmitted longitudinally from one particle to the next in the same direction as the advancing wave front. The factors that influence velocity of transmission are mass of the moving particles

Table 2-3   *Molar Refractivity R_D (Na D line) for Pure Halides* [a]

	Solid	Infinitely dilute solution	Gaseous ions	Molten salt
NaCl	8.26	9.27	9.5	9.48 (850°C)
KCl	10.50	11.30	11.3	11.60 (800°C)
CdCl₂	—	20.44	20.56	21.3 (650°C)
PbCl₂	26.85	—	—	29.3 (600°C)

[a] From Bloom and Peryer. [5]

and distance over which they move before colliding with another carrier. Thus the free volume from ultrasonic velocity measurements is the fluctuation volume or volume in which an ion can move in its cage. The other 85% of the volume increase on melting must be present in the form of holes, which take no part in the transmission of ultrasonic vibrations since an ion, on meeting any of the numerous holes, cannot transmit its energy into the hole, and this results in the need for the advancing wave front to be propagated by the other ions not adjacent to holes.

Table 2-4 shows fluctuation volume for some molten alkali chlorides (results of Bockris and Richards [6]).

In molten salts, heat is transferred in much the same manner as sound, giving rise to alternative calculations of fluctuation volume from measurements of thermal conductivity (Turnbull [7] and Bloom et al.[8]). The results have been found to be very close to those calculated for the same molten salts from ultrasonic velocity measurements (see Section 5-6).

2-4 THEORETICAL INTERPRETATION OF MOLTEN SALTS

Theoretical calculations of the physical properties of molten salts have obvious value but in view of the complications associated with the theoretical interpretation of liquids, it is necessary in practice to invent for molten salts approximate models that are capable of mathematical solution. Basically, two types of models have been used: (a) models based on the crystal lattice and (b) models in which no lattice is implied.

Lattice Theories

These have been extensively developed by Kirkwood,[9] Hirschfelder,[10] and others. Lattice theories or cell theories are based on the subdivision of the physical space occupied by the liquid into a number of cells or small volume elements arranged in the form of a regular lattice as in Fig. 2-6 in the two-dimensional representation of NaCl. The change from solid to

Table 2-4 *Fluctuation Volume V_f per Mole and Molar Volume V in Molten Alkali Chlorides at 900°C*

Salt	V_f (ml)	V (ml)
LiCl	0.92	30.8
NaCl	0.62	38.9
KCl	0.72	51.4
CsCl	1.45	66.8

liquid can be accomplished in two ways: (1) by removing from the lattice the correct number of ions of each sign to represent the correct decrease of density on melting, while leaving the others substantially within the same cells as in the solid. Such a rearrangement would not reproduce the observed changes in interionic distances and loss of long-range order on melting. (2) By removing the correct number of ions and rearranging the others in a more drastic fashion than under (1). Although it is self evident that the established data for average interionic distance and coordination number could be represented in this way, the experimental observance of complete loss of long-range order on melting is quite incompatible with lattice theories unless the lattice becomes so distorted as to lose its significance.

Regardless of the physical unreality of lattice theories, they provide, in principle, the simplest path to theoretical calculation of physical properties of molten salts.

Other Theories

The hole theory of liquids. The hole theory has been developed by Frenkel,[11] Altar,[12] and Fürth.[13] Bockris and Richards [6] applied it to a description of molten salts. The theory relies on the application of macroscopic fluid dynamics to the surface and surroundings of holes, which are constantly changing both their size and position in the liquid. The theory requires the evaporation of particles of liquid into holes where they exist as vapor, and the calculation of surface energy of holes from the macroscopic surface tension. Calculations using the equations derived from it lead to the conclusion that the average size of the holes is usually too small even to accommodate one particle, let alone the vapor of the substance; hence the theory is somewhat artificial. Nevertheless, the qualitative picture presented by the hole theory is in accordance with experiment.

Cybotactic and significant structure theories. A theory that enables a qualitative explanation of most of the physical properties of liquids is the *cybotactic* or *microcrystalline* theory introduced by Stewart.[14] The liquid is pictured as submicroscopic sections of crystal lattice able to move by sliding over one another. Thus short-range order is preserved without the concomitant long-range order of the solid. Difficulties exist in the quantitative interpretation of this theory.

In the *significant structure theory* of Eyring et al.,[15] the fragments of crystal lattice are separated by a compressed gas of the same substance. The thermodynamic properties of the liquid can be deduced by deriving a partition function consisting of part due to solid and part due to the gas. Although the theory is quite successful in predicting many physical properties of molten salts, it is somewhat artificial and, in addition, relies for its numerical evaluation on two parameters that, being inaccessible by theoretical evaluation alone, have the effect of being adjustable. The theory nevertheless is very useful for predicting molten salt properties. A review of the above and other theories is given by Bloom and Bockris.[16]

Bonding in Simple Melts

For the molten alkali halides, the forces between ions are largely coulombic, hence each ion tends to attract an environment of oppositely charged ions. With molten group IIA halides, however, there is less certainty regarding their structure and it is difficult to formulate a general pattern. Beryllium chloride, with its high vapor pressure, low electrical conductance, and short liquidus range (107°), is apparently largely covalent but dissociates to simpler ionic species with increase of temperature. The other group IIA chlorides, although having a much greater degree of ionic character, tend to form ion association complexes on melting with further dissociation to simple ions on increasing temperature. Thus

$$MX_2 \rightleftharpoons MX^+ + X^- \rightleftharpoons M^{2+} + 2X^-$$

The zinc halides form network structures in the molten state with very high viscosity and very low electrical conductance—thus the proportion of free ions is very low just above the melting point. Increase of temperature causes a rapid breakdown of the network and considerably increases the proportion of free ions. The postulated effect of melting solid zinc chloride and the production of simpler species is shown in Fig. 2-8. Figure 2-8a shows the crystal structure of $ZnCl_2$, which has a layer structure with a coordination number of 4. Melting would cause the network structure to break up, as in Fig. 2-8b, with production of simpler species, such as the tetrahedral complex ions $ZnCl_4^{2-}$, in equilibrium with larger sections of the network to form a viscous melt. At higher temperatures progressive degradation of the network is thought to produce first larger proportions of complex ions (including $ZnCl_3^-$ and $ZnCl^+$) and, at still higher temperatures, the simple ionic species Zn^{2+} and $2Cl^-$. Although the proposed model for the degraded structure Fig. 2-8b shows fragments with the same geometrical arrangement as the original tetrahedral structure, that is, with $ZnCl_3^-$ pyramidal and $ZnCl_2$ bent, the Cl–Cl repulsions would tend to make these groups planar and linear, respectively.

A more detailed discussion on the structure of molten halides will be given in later chapters.

2-5 BONDING IN MIXTURES OF MOLTEN HALIDES

In addition to simple ions and associated ionic species such as MX^+, mixtures of molten salts may also have as structural units *complex ions* in

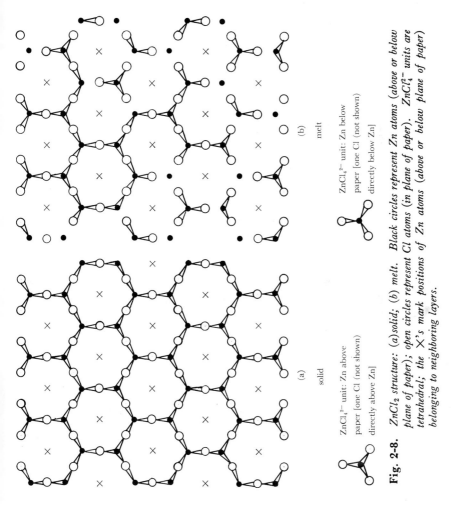

(a)

solid

ZnCl₄²⁻ unit: Zn above
paper [one Cl (not shown)
directly above Zn]

(b)

melt

ZnCl₄²⁻ unit: Zn below
paper [one Cl (not shown)
directly below Zn]

Fig. 2-8. *ZnCl₂ structure: (a) solid; (b) melt. Black circles represent Zn atoms (above or below plane of paper); open circles represent Cl atoms (in plane of paper). ZnCl₄²⁻ units are tetrahedral; the X's mark positions of Zn atoms (above or below plane of paper) belonging to neighboring layers.*

which the bonding is partly covalent. Thus in molten mixtures of cadmium chloride and potassium chloride, the ions $CdCl_3^-$, $CdCl_4^{2-}$, and $CdCl_6^{4-}$ have been suggested. Evidence for the formation of complex ions in the various molten salt systems will be given following a discussion of the various physical methods of investigation.

2-6 MOLTEN SALTS WITH POLYMERIZED ANIONS

Molten mixtures of metal oxides have been investigated for quite some time owing to their industrial importance, e.g., as slags in steel making. They consist typically of an alkali metal oxide, such as Na_2O, in mixture with SiO_2 in various proportions. Other acidic oxides leading to similar electrolytes are B_2O_3 and P_2O_5. They have a number of common properties, which have been summarized by Bloom and Bockris.[16] These properties include (a) high equivalent conductance increasing with decrease of cation size to a certain size and then decreasing with further decrease of cation size. The conductance is completely ionic for the alkali and alkaline earth cations. (b) The heat of activation for viscosity is approximately constant for 0.1–0.6 mole fraction M_2O. (c) Expansivity becomes zero at less than 0.1 mole fraction M_2O, but increases with mole fraction M_2O above that concentration. (d) Compressibility increases on addition of M_2O to SiO_2 up to 0.15 mole fraction M_2O, then remains approximately constant up to 0.5 mole fraction. All these facts are consistent with the formation of polyanions in the molten mixtures.

Models for the Polyanions

In liquid mixtures of metal oxides and, say, SiO_2, it has been established by Bockris and co-workers [16] that O^{2-} is not a current-transporting ion. Polymeric anions based on the SiO_4^{n-} monomer are the inferred structural units.

In the molten mixtures that have composition equal to that of the orthosilicate (i.e., $2M_2O \cdot SiO_2$), discrete SiO_4^{4-} ions are formed, but addition of more SiO_2 causes polymerization of SiO_4^{4-} first to $^{-3}O_3Si$—O—SiO_3^{3-}. On further increase of the SiO_2/M_2O ratio, the chain length increases. Near 0.5 mole fraction a large increase of chain length would occur (—Si—O—Si— chains would be coiled in an analogous manner to chains in organic polymers), and to avoid this, ring formation would commence. Ring types possible are $Si_3O_9^{6-}$ and $Si_4O_{12}^{8-}$. Further addition of SiO_2 to the 0.5 mole fraction composition is thought to lead to $Si_6O_{15}^{6-}$ and $Si_8O_{20}^{8-}$, which are essentially dimeric forms of the simple rings formed at the 1:1 composition. Further polymerization would account for the properties of the melts on adding additional SiO_2 until a three-dimensional network structure began to be formed.

On increasing the proportion of SiO_2, the increased polymerization of SiO_4^{4-} tetrahedra to form ring and network structures accounts for the physical properties of these mixtures to the composition $M_2O \cdot 2SiO_2$ but at higher proportions of SiO_2, islets or *icebergs* of vitreous SiO_2 are thought to be formed in addition to polyanions.   Below 0.12 mole fraction M_2O most of the SiO_2 would be in the form of the SiO_2 islets but at larger proportions of M_2O there would be an increasing proportion of polyanions.   At 0.2 mole fraction M_2O the radius of an iceberg would be about 19 Å (assumed spherical). The combination of icebergs and polyanions accounts for the properties of the $M_2O + SiO_2$ systems from 0 to 0.33 mole fraction M_2O, particularly the almost constant partial molar volume of SiO_2 observed in this region of composition.   At the upper limit of this composition range, the icebergs would have a radius of about 6 Å and would then be identical with polyanions already proposed at this composition.

REFERENCES

1. Ubbelohde, A. R., *Proc. Chem. Soc.*, 332 (1960).
2. Lark-Horowitz, K., and Miller, E. P., *Phys. Rev.*, **49**, 418 (1936); **51**, 61 (1937).
3. Zarzycki, J., *J. Phys. Radium (Suppl. Phys. Appl.)*, **18**, 65A (1957); **19**, 13A (1958).
4. Levy, H. A., Agron, P. A., Bredig, M. A., and Danford, M. D., *Ann. N.Y. Acad. Sci.*, **79**, 762 (1960).
5. Bloom, H., and Peryer, B. M., *Aust. J. Chem.*, **18**, 777 (1965).
6. Bockris, J. O'M., and Richards, N. E., *Proc. Roy. Soc.*, **A241**, 44 (1957).
7. Turnbull, A. G., *Aust. J. Appl. Sci.*, **12**, 30, 324 (1961).
8. Bloom, H., Doroszkowski, A., and Tricklebank, S. B., *Aust. J. Chem.*, **18**, 1171 (1965).
9. Kirkwood, J. G., *J. Chem. Phys.*, **3**, 300 (1935); *Chem. Rev.*, **19**, 275 (1936); **18**, 380 (1950).
10. Hirschfelder, J. O., *J. Chem. Ed.*, **16**, 540 (1939).
11. Frenkel, J., *The Kinetic Theory of Liquids*, Oxford University Press, London and New York, 1946.
12. Altar, W., *J. Chem. Phys.*, **5**, 577 (1937).
13. Fürth, R., *Proc. Camb. Phil. Soc.*, **37**, 252 (1941).
14. Stewart, G. W., *Phys. Rev.*, **30**, 232 (1927).
15. Carlson, C. M., Eyring, H., and Ree, T., *Proc. Natl. Acad. Sci.*, **46**, 333 (1960); Eyring, H., Ree, T., and Hirai, N., *Proc. Natl. Acad. Sci.*, **44**, 683 (1958).
16. Bloom, H., and Bockris, J. O'M., in *Fused Salts* (B. R. Sundheim, ed.), Chapter I, McGraw-Hill, New York, 1964.

3

The Solvent Properties of
Molten Salts

The excellent solvent properties of molten salts give rise to their main industrial uses but at the same time are the cause of the corrosive action that makes for difficulties in their application.

3-1 SOLUTIONS OF GASES, NONMETALS, AND ORGANIC COMPOUNDS

Gases That Dissolve without Chemical Interaction

Many gases are soluble to a small extent in most molten salts, and in systems that do not react chemically the dissolved gas is liberated unchanged on solidification or by reducing the pressure. As for conventional liquid solvents, the solubility of the gas is directly proportional to pressure (Henry's law) and increases with increase of temperature. (Allowance must be made for any interaction with the solvent.)

Carbon dioxide dissolves in molten alkali halides to give simple solutions and its solubility at a constant temperature increases in the same direction as increasing free volume of the salt. At 950°C the solubility at 1 atm pressure is 7.0×10^{-6} mole CO_2 per milliliter of KCl compared with 4.0×10^{-6} for NaCl.

The noble gases have been found to be soluble in mixtures of molten fluorides (Grimes et al.[1]) and thus the mass of He, Ne, Ar, or Xe dissolved is proportional to pressure in accordance with Henry's law. The noble gases of higher molecular weight are less soluble than those of lower molecular weight. Solubility increases with increase of temperature. For example, He dissolves in a molten mixture of 0.53 mole fraction NaF + ZrF_4 at 600°C to the extent of 32.3×10^{-8} mole He per milliliter of melt at 1.53 atm saturating gas pressure, rising to 61.4×10^{-8} mole He per milliliter of melt at 800°C and the same pressure.

Gases That Dissolve with Chemical Interaction

Some gases react with the molten salt solvent, giving very much greater solubilities; thus a mixture of 0.25 mole $CuCl_2$ and 0.75 mole KCl can dissolve 0.75 mole fluorine by the reaction

$$2CuCl_2 + 6KCl + 6F_2 = 2K_3CuF_6 + 5Cl_2$$

Titanium tetrachloride will dissolve very slowly below 800°C in a molten equimolar mixture of NaCl + KCl to at least 14% at atmospheric pressure due to the reaction

$$TiCl_4 + 2KCl = K_2TiCl_6$$

Hydrogen fluoride is also very soluble in fluoride melts; its solubility decreases with increase of temperature, indicating that chemical reaction has taken place with the solvent.

The Solubility of Water

In the molten LiCl + KCl eutectic mixture, the solubility of water is proportional to pressure in accordance with Henry's law up to 18 mm pressure at 480°C, but at higher temperatures there is evidence of hydrolysis of LiCl. Molten lithium chloride, as well as zinc chloride and some other salts, tends to retain some water at temperatures even as high as 1000°C. The unusual tenacity of retention of water, for example, by Li^+, is due to its high charge density, and evacuation even for long periods does not remove all the water.

In contrast, water can be removed quantitatively but slowly by evacuation of most melts, e.g., NaCl + KCl. The water dissolved in alkali nitrates is apparently accommodated in the interstices. The optimum practical method for dehydration of salts is to evacuate the solid powder for long intervals at increasing temperature up to the melting point. The rate of loss of water decreases markedly when the salt melts.

Nonmetallic Elements

Few investigations have been carried out using nonmetallic elements as solutes, but it has been established that both sulfur and iodine are soluble in many molten salts. In both molten LiCl + KCl and LiBr + KBr eutectics, sulfur dissolves to form blue paramagnetic solutions that have similar absorption spectra, showing there is no specific interaction with the halide ion. The most probable form of the solute is the diatomic molecule S_2.

On the other hand, iodine dissolves readily, to the extent of 10^{-4}–10^{-3} molar, in the LiI + KI and LiCl + KCl eutectics by reaction with the solvent forming I_3^- in the first case and I_2Cl^- in the second.

Organic Compounds

There is much indirect evidence of the solubility of organic materials in molten salts that are used as solvents for reactions between gaseous organic materials (Sundermeyer [2]). The type of reaction achieved is influenced considerably by the properties of the solvent in much the same way as in conventional solvents. Most organic materials, however, decompose at the temperature of the solvent and quantitative information on solubility is not available. The success of molten salts as solvents for reacting organic species depends on the rapid rate of reactions and high yields achieved; thus contact times of a fraction of a second are adequate in many instances. Under such conditions very little decomposition is observed. A brief discussion of some organic reactions in molten salt solvents will be given in Chapter 9. Methanol and nitrobenzene are known to form stable solutions in molten lithium chlorate. 1,2-Dibromoethane has been shown to be miscible with $AlBr_3$ and KBr mixtures to form liquid solutions over a wide range of compositions. In these mixtures, complex compounds, $Al_2Br_6 \cdot nKBr$, are formed. The bromides also form liquid mixtures with toluene and xylene. Aniline, acetone, benzene, and 1,2,4-triazole have also been shown to form liquid mixtures with quite a variety of inorganic salts.

3-2 SOLUTIONS OF METALS

Molten salts are good solvents for metals. This was noted by Bunsen and Kirchoff as early as 1861 during the electrolysis of molten rubidium and cesium chlorides, when a coloration of the melt by the dissolved metals was observed.

Generally, molten salts take on an intense coloration on dissolving the metal; for example, sodium dissolves in molten sodium halides to give deep blue solutions and cadmium in cadmium halides to give intense red solutions. The solubility varies widely. Tin and thallium have very low solubility in their respective molten halides (approx. 0.01 mole %), but many molten sulfides dissolve more than 50 mole % metal and can at a high enough temperature form completely miscible systems.

Metals are generally soluble only in the salts of that metal, although displacement solubility can also take place. Thus potassium dissolves in molten sodium chloride by the reaction

$$K + NaCl \rightleftharpoons Na + KCl$$

The KCl produced is miscible with NaCl and the solution thus contains ions of both metals.

Solutions of metals in molten salts can be divided into two main groups, one in which there is no chemical interaction and the other in which reaction takes place. A more detailed discussion of metal solubility will be given in Chapter 8.

3-3   SOLUTIONS OF OTHER SALTS

Salt solutions may be classified into groups which vary according to the number of variables introduced into the composition of the system on mixing. The simplest is the binary mixture, such as KCl + NaCl, NaCl + NaF, and so on. In such systems, AX + BX and AX + AY, respectively, the composition of the melt remains constant in terms of one (common) ion, but varies in terms of the other. Ternary systems with a common ion may be represented by AX + AY + AZ, and so on. Systems of two salts with no ion in common lead to variation in composition with respect to all four ions on changing the proportions of salts in the mixture. Such systems, represented by AX + BY, are known as *reciprocal systems*. Reciprocal systems may be composed of more than two salts, e.g., AX + BY + CZ. A more detailed discussion of salt systems will be given in Chapter 4.

Incomplete Miscibility

Most molten salt systems are completely miscible in all proportions at a suitably high temperature. There are, however, many systems in which there is only partial miscibility of the individual melts, and in such cases the condensed phases in equilibrium could include two liquids of different composition. Systems involving two salts with incomplete miscibility in the liquid phase may be summarized as follows:

1. $AX + BX$ (*binary*) *systems*, in which one component is covalent and has Al^{3+}, Bi^{3+}, Sb^{3+}, or another multivalent cation, while the other component is a typically ionic salt. Examples are $AlBr_3 + CaBr_2$, $AlCl_3 + KCl$.

2. $AX + AY$ (*binary*) *systems*, in which the anions are of considerably different size and charge density. Examples are $NaCl$ + sodium silicate, titanate, or borate.

3. $AX + BY$ (*reciprocal*) *systems*, in which one of the components is a salt of low polarity (i.e., covalent) or the halide, oxide, or sulfide of a transition or posttransition metal and the other component is a typically ionic salt. Examples of this group include $AlBr_3 + NaCl$ and $AgBr + LiNO_3$.

In some cases both components may be typical salts: for example, $LiF + CsCl$ and $LiF + CsBr$, which have incomplete miscibility in the molten state.

3-4 SOLUTIONS OF OXIDES

Salt melts dissolve oxides to a certain extent. The following generalizations apply for solutions of oxides of the first transition series in molten $NaCl$ at 900°C.

(a) Only oxides of metals with an odd atomic number dissolve to any appreciable extent.

(b) Solubilities range from 0.001 to 0.01 mole fraction of oxide (except for copper oxide).

(c) With the exception of V_2O_5, metals with soluble oxides must also have another oxide stable at the temperature concerned.

(d) For oxide solutions, the metal-to-oxygen ratios found in the melts do not correspond to any known oxide stable in the solid, hence chemical reaction with the solvent occurs. Some salt + oxide systems also have regions of partial liquid miscibility. These include PbO with either LiF, NaF, KF, $NaCl$, KCl, $RbCl$, $NaBr$, or KI, respectively, and B_2O_3 with $NaCl$ or KCl, respectively.

SUGGESTED READING

"Molten Salts as Solvents," H. Bloom and J. W. Hastie, in *Non-Aqueous Solvent Systems* (T. C. Waddington, ed.), Academic Press, London, 1965.

REFERENCES

1. Grimes, W. R., Smith, N. V., and Watson, G. M., *J. Phys. Chem.*, **62**, 862 (1958).
2. Sundermeyer, W., *Angew. Chem. Intern. Ed. Engl.*, **4**, 222 (1965).

4

Thermodynamics of Molten Salt Systems

For practical purposes, thermodynamic properties are among the most important for the characterization of chemical systems. They also lend themselves to the testing of structural models and this aspect has particular relevance for molten salt mixtures.

4-1 THERMODYNAMIC FUNCTIONS

A knowledge will be assumed of elementary thermodynamics together with the following thermodynamic functions and variables.

Internal energy U

Enthalpy (heat content) H

Gibbs free energy G

Helmholtz free energy A

Entropy S

Heat capacity C (C_p at constant pressure, C_v at constant volume)

Number of moles n

Mole fraction, $x\left(x_i = \dfrac{n_i}{\Sigma_i n_i}; \ \Sigma_i x_i = 1\right)$

Pressure P
Temperature T (degrees absolute)
Volume V
Gas constant R

The Thermodynamic Activity

For ideal gases an expansion from pressure P_1 to P_2 results in the free energy change

$$G_1 - G_2 = RT \ln\left(\frac{P_1}{P_2}\right) \tag{4-1}$$

For real gases this equation is not applicable, but for P a quantity ϕ, called by Lewis the *fugacity*, can be substituted. Thus

$$G_1 - G_2 = RT \ln\left(\frac{\phi_1}{\phi_2}\right) \tag{4-2}$$

The fugacity is therefore the pressure that a real gas would exert if it were to behave thermodynamically as an ideal gas. For real gases and for salt vapors at low pressures Eq. (4-1) gives satisfactory agreement with experiment. The activity a_i for any component is defined as

$$a_i = \frac{\phi_i}{\phi_i^0} \tag{4-3}$$

$$= \frac{P_i}{P_i^0} \tag{4-4}$$

for gases at reasonably low pressures.

The quantities ϕ^0 and P^0 are the fugacity and partial pressure, respectively, of the gas in its standard state. For molten salt mixtures, P^0 is taken as the vapor pressure of the pure molten salt at the temperature under consideration, that is, the pure molten salt is taken as constituting its standard state. The activity of a component of the mixture in its standard state is thus taken to be unity.

Partial and Integral Thermodynamic Quantities

Partial molal or molar quantities, e.g., $\bar{G}_1$, $\bar{H}_1$, $\bar{S}_1$, are defined as the rate of increase of the particular thermodynamic quantity with increase of concentration of a particular component of the mixture, all other variables being held constant. For example, partial molar enthalpy of component 1 of a mixture is given by

$$\bar{H}_1 = \left(\frac{\partial H}{\partial n_1}\right)_{T,P,n_2,n_3,\,\ldots}$$

where n_2, n_3, and so on are the number of moles of the other components and T, P are kept constant. Partial molar free energy is known also as chemical potential and is often given the symbol μ. For example

$$\bar{G}_1 = \mu_1 = \bar{A}_1$$

Frequently used thermodynamic relationships are

$$G = H - TS \qquad (4\text{-}5)$$
$$A = U - TS \qquad (4\text{-}6)$$

The Gibbs-Duhem Equation

Many experimental methods involving the measurement of thermodynamic quantities for molten salt mixtures result in the evaluation of partial molar quantities for one component. For a solution consisting of only two components, it is in fact necessary to measure partial molar quantities pertaining to one component only. For the other, the quantities can be evaluated by means of the Gibbs-Duhem equation

$$n_1\,d\bar{G}_1 + n_2\,d\bar{G}_2 = 0 \qquad (4\text{-}7)$$

This equation can be transformed to

$$x_1\,d\bar{G}_1 + x_2\,d\bar{G}_2 = 0 \qquad (4\text{-}8)$$

For a solution of more than two components

$$x_1\,d\bar{G}_1 + x_2\,d\bar{G}_2 + x_3\,d\bar{G}_3 + \cdots = 0 \qquad (4\text{-}9)$$

and there are analogous equations for each of the other partial molar quantities. Applications of the Gibbs-Duhem equation will be discussed later in this chapter.

Ideal Binary Liquid Mixtures

An ideal binary solution may be defined as one for which the activity of each component equals its mole fraction over the whole composition range.

Thus for an ideal binary solution, for example, two molten salts with a common ion

$$a_1 = \frac{P_1}{P_1{}^0} = x_1 \qquad (4\text{-}10)$$

which is Raoult's law.

From integration of the Gibbs-Duhem equation it is found that for the other component of the ideal solution

$$a_2 = kx_2 \qquad (k \text{ is a constant}) \qquad (4\text{-}11)$$

giving Henry's law.

For each component, equations for the increase of partial molar free energy upon transfer of 1 mole from the pure liquid to a solution of sufficient volume that the composition remains constant are

$$\Delta \bar{G}_1 = \bar{G}_1 - G_1{}^0 = RT \ln x_1 \qquad (4\text{-}12)$$
$$\Delta \bar{G}_2 = \bar{G}_2 - G_2{}^0 = RT \ln x_2 \qquad (4\text{-}13)$$

where $\bar{G}_1$ is the partial molar free energy of component 1 in the solution and $G_1{}^0$ is the free energy of the pure liquid, that is, in its standard state. The free energy of mixing for n_1 moles of component 1 and n_2 moles of component 2 is given by

$$\Delta G_{\mathrm{mix}} = n_1 \Delta \bar{G}_1 + n_2 \Delta \bar{G}_2$$
$$= RT(n_1 \ln x_1 + n_2 \ln x_2) \qquad (4\text{-}14)$$

Also as

$$S = -\left(\frac{\partial G}{\partial T}\right)_P,$$

$$\Delta S_{\mathrm{mix}} = -\left(\frac{\partial \Delta G_{\mathrm{mix}}}{\partial T}\right)_P = -R(n_1 \ln x_1 + n_2 \ln x_2) \qquad (4\text{-}15)$$

And since

$$H = G + TS,$$
$$\Delta H_{\mathrm{mix}} = 0$$

Similarly, $\Delta V_{\mathrm{mix}} = 0$ for an ideal solution.

Nonideal Binary Solutions

For nonideal solutions, ΔH_{mix} and ΔV_{mix} are not zero and the activity of any component is not equal to its mole fraction. An activity coefficient is defined such that

$$\gamma_i = \frac{a_i}{x_i} \qquad (4\text{-}16)$$

For a nonideal binary solution

$$\Delta \bar{G}_1 = \bar{G}_1 - G_1{}^0 = RT \ln a_1 = RT \ln x_1 + RT \ln \gamma_1 \qquad (4\text{-}17)$$

and

$$\Delta\bar{G}_2 = \bar{G}_2 - G_2^0 = RT \ln a_2 = RT \ln x_2 + RT \ln \gamma_2 \qquad (4\text{-}18)$$
$$\therefore \Delta G_{\text{mix}} = RT(x_1 \ln a_1 + x_2 \ln a_2) \qquad (\text{per mole})$$
$$= RT(x_1 \ln x_1 + x_2 \ln x_2) + RT(x_1 \ln \gamma_1 + x_2 \ln \gamma_2) \qquad (4\text{-}19)$$

From (4-19), the first term on the right-hand side is the ideal free energy of mixing. The second term is known as the *excess free energy of mixing,* ΔG_{mix}^E (which may be abbreviated as G^E); that is,

$$G^E = \Delta G_{\text{mix}}^E = RT(x_1 \ln \gamma_1 + x_2 \ln \gamma_2) \qquad (4\text{-}20)$$

and the partial excess free energy of each component of the mixture is given by

$$\bar{G}_1^E = RT \ln \gamma_1 \qquad \bar{G}_2^E = RT \ln \gamma_2 \qquad (4\text{-}21)$$

The excess integral and partial enthalpy, entropy, and molar volume are also frequently used for molten salt mixtures.

Regular Solutions

For many nonideal solutions Hildebrand found that a simple pattern applies. Thus for such a binary solution

$$\log \gamma_1 = \frac{b}{RT} x_2^2 \qquad (4\text{-}22)$$

and

$$\log \gamma_2 = \frac{b}{RT} x_1^2 \qquad (4\text{-}23)$$

where b has the same value for both components of the solutions, independent of composition and temperature. Such solutions are said to be *regular* and their formation from the pure components involves ideal entropy of mixing but a nonzero heat of mixing.

4-2 THE MELTING OF CRYSTALLINE SALTS

In melting, the ordered solid becomes a considerably disordered liquid (cf. Figs. 2-6 and 2-7). For crystals of the noble gases, the positional disorder on melting obeys laws of similitude and in all cases the entropy of melting is about 3.3 eu. In these cases $\Delta V_{\text{fus}}/V_s$ is about 0.15.

For ionic crystals with spherical noble gas type ions the positional disorder on melting will include processes other than those involved on melting noble gas crystals because the particles are charged and electrical interactions between positive and negative particles will tend to form arrangements of high local order within the melt. This causes shrinkage of average distance between unlike ions and an expansion of the overall lattice to lessen repulsion effects. Hence ionic melts contain microregions where the density is either below or above that of the ideal crystal lattice but the regions of lower density clearly predominate.

Heat of Fusion

Fusion requires less energy than vaporization. Thus for NaCl, $\Delta H_{fus} =$ 6.69 kcal mole^{-1} compared with $\Delta H_{vap} = 45.3$ kcal mole^{-1}. This reflects the much greater forces required to produce completely separate pairs of ions than those required to produce the relatively minor degree of disorder during melting.

Entropy of Fusion

The entropy of fusion of an ionic crystal includes contributions from holes, interstitial holes, paired holes, and paired ions, together with cooperative defects extending over more than two holes. In some salts, such as those of Ag, Zn, Cd, the entropy of formation of association complexes may be very important; for example, Cd^{2+} may tend to form $CdCl^+$, $CdCl_3^-$, and so on, in melts containing $CdCl_2$.

Table 4-1 gives values of heat and entropy of fusion of a number of halides. The values of ΔS_{fus} can be seen in general to be somewhat less per ion than the value of 3.3 eu for the noble gas crystals.

Table 4-1   *Heat and Entropy of Fusion of Molten Alkali Halides*

Salt	T_{fus} (°K)	ΔH_{fus} (kcal mole^{-1})	ΔS_{fus} (eu)
LiCl	883	4.76	5.39
NaCl	1074	6.69	6.23
KCl	1043	6.34	6.08
RbCl	995	5.67	5.70
CsCl	918	4.84	5.27
LiBr	823	4.22	5.13
NaBr	1020	6.24	6.12
KBr	1007	6.10	6.06
RbBr	965	5.57	5.77
CsBr	909	5.64	6.20
LiI	742	3.50	4.72
NaI	933	5.64	6.04
KI	954	5.74	6.02
RbI	920	5.27	5.73
CsI	899	5.64	6.27

4-3   THE PHASE RULE

For a system of C components, the phase rule of J. Willard Gibbs limits the number of degrees of freedom F for the coexistence of $\wp$ phases to

$$F = C + 2 - \wp$$

Vapor is not counted as a phase for condensed systems and pressure is usually taken as constant (atmospheric); hence, for $\wp$ condensed phases

$$F = C + 1 - \wp \qquad \text{(pressure = constant)}$$

Binary Salt Systems

For a salt system of two chemical components the maximum number of condensed phases at constant pressure that can coexist in equilibrium at a fixed temperature and composition is 3.   Such an invariant point is illustrated on the phase diagram of the $PbCl_2 + NaCl$ system in Fig. 4-1 as the eutectic point E, which represents the mixture that has a minimum melting point at constant pressure.   The curved lines AE and EB represent the equilibria between molten $NaCl + PbCl_2$ mixtures and pure solid $PbCl_2$ or $NaCl$, respectively.   Thus the limit of stability of liquid phase is given by AEB, which is known as the liquidus curve.   The compositions of the solids are given by the solidus lines, in this case AC and BD, representing pure $PbCl_2$ and pure $NaCl$, respectively.   In the area AEC, solid $PbCl_2$ is in equilibrium with melt $(PbCl_2 + NaCl)$ of composition given by the liquidus along AE, while in the area BED, solid $NaCl$ is in equilibrium with melt of composition given by liquidus along BE.   Below CED, the solids pure $PbCl_2 + NaCl$ are the only stable phases and the liquid phase is nonexistent.

Figure 4-1 represents a simple system.   In actual practice the solidus is often not a pure component but solid solutions of one component in the other. Polymorphic transitions can cause further complications.

Another simple binary system, $NaCl + KCl$, is shown in Fig. 4-2.   In this there is simple mixing with the formation of a continuous range of solid solutions for which there is a minimum melting point at 50 mole % KCl.

Figure 4-3 for the $CaCl_2 + KCl$ system illustrates a more complex phase diagram which can be broken down into two simple eutectic systems.   The maximum melting point salt mixture at 50 mole % KCl thus behaves as a component solid salt and as such separates from the 50 mole % liquid mixture as the compound $CaCl_2 \cdot KCl$.   A compound with a maximum melting point such as $CaCl_2 \cdot KCl$ is known as a *congruently melting compound*.

In Fig. 4-4 for the $PbCl_2 + KCl$ system, a congruently melting compound $2PbCl_2 \cdot KCl$ is formed from the melt at 0.333 mole fraction (i.e.,

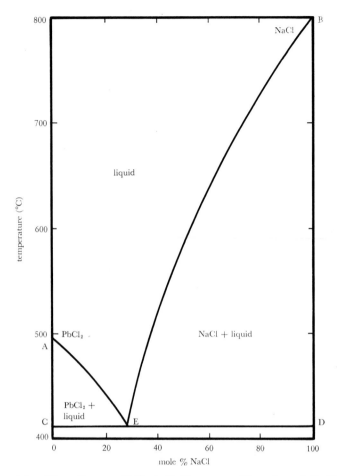

Fig. 4-1.   *Phase diagram: PbCl₂ + NaCl system.   (From data of K. Freis, Neues Jahrb. Mineral, **37**, 766 (1914).)*

$33\frac{1}{3}$ mole %) KCl.   In addition, the phase diagram shows the formation of another compound, $PbCl_2 \cdot 2KCl$, at 0.667 mole fraction KCl, which decomposes below its melting point—hence the liquidus curve does not show a maximum at this composition.   Such compounds are said to be *incongruently melting* and their appearance in the phase diagram is observable by an invariant halt (often called a *peritectic point*) in determination of cooling curves during thermal analyses.

Phase diagrams may show even greater complexity, as in Fig. 4-5 for the $PbCl_2 + RbCl$ system, where there are three congruently melting com-

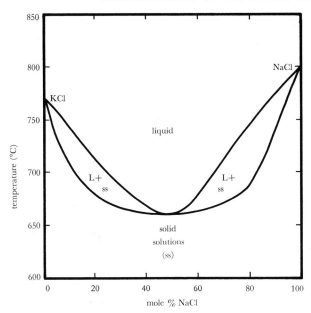

Fig. 4-2. *Phase diagram: KCl + NaCl system.* (*From data of W. P. Radischtschew, J. Gen. Chem. USSR,* **5,** *455 (1935).)*

pounds, as indicated by the three melting point maxima. For halides of the multivalent metals in mixture with alkali halides with a common anion, phase diagrams become increasingly complex as the size of the alkali cation increases. Thus $PbCl_2 + NaCl$ forms a eutectic only, $PbCl_2 + KCl$ has two compounds, while both $PbCl_2 + RbCl$ and $PbCl_2 + CsCl$ have three compounds. Many intermediate compounds are naturally occurring and cryolite, Na_3AlF_6, is shown in Fig. 4-6 as the congruently melting compound $AlF_3 \cdot 3NaF$ with a melting point maximum at 0.25 mole fraction AlF_3. This complex salt is of particular importance commercially as it is the main component of the molten solvent for the electrolytic extraction of aluminum (see Chapter 9).

Ternary Salt Systems

Additive ternary systems forming no compound. Additive ternary systems are those with three salts, all with either common cation or common anion; an example is the system KF + KCl + KI, whose phase diagram is shown in two different ways in Figs. 4-7 and 4-8, respectively. Ternary

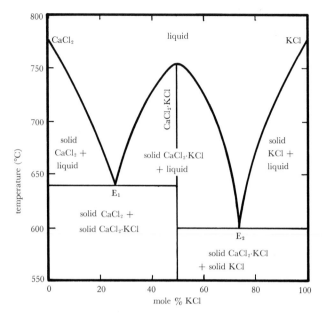

Fig. 4-3. *Phase diagram: CaCl₂ + KCl system.* (*From data of K. Scholich, Neues Jahrb. Mineral,* **43,** *251 (1920).*)

additive systems require three composition axes for their representation in addition to a temperature axis (at constant pressure); hence, a three-dimensional model, shown in perspective in Fig. 4-7, can be used. According to the phase rule the ternary system can have 3 degrees of freedom for any single phase; hence the liquidus is represented as surfaces rather than lines as in binary systems. A ternary additive system can of course be regarded as a welding of three binary systems which form the three vertical faces of the three-dimensional model.

In Fig. 4-7 the three individual binary systems each have their own eutectics, E_1, E_2, and E_3, respectively, while E_4 represents the ternary eutectic. Ternary eutectics are very useful for the formation of heat treatment baths, for example, in the descaling of metals and for heat transfer media. The curves E_1E_4, E_2E_4, and E_3E_4 represent the lowering of the binary eutectic temperatures by the third solute. Above the surfaces at any particular composition, the system consists of unsaturated liquid. Below each surface, liquid and solid equilibria may exist.

Detailed discussion of the properties of ternary systems is better carried out with the aid of perspective projections, as in Fig. 4-8 for the KF + KCl + KI system. This orthogonal projection on the composition plane is known

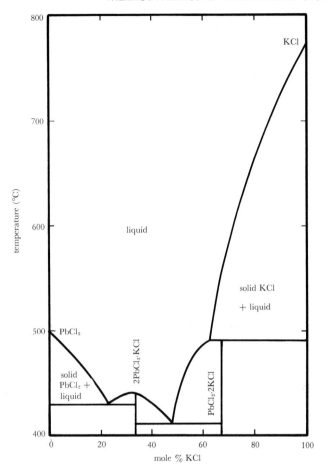

Fig. 4-4.   *Phase diagram: PbCl₂ + KCl system.   (From data of Ja. A. Ugai and W. A. Shatillo, J. Phys. Chem. USSR, 23, 744 (1949).)*

as a *polythermal projection*, or simply the phase diagram, and is divided into three fields representing the regions of composition of the ternary liquid mixture in which one particular pure salt crystallizes out first on cooling.   In Fig. 4-8 the KF field, for example, is bounded by the KF apex of the triangle, the eutectics of freezing points 605°C and 547°C, respectively, and the ternary eutectic of freezing point 488°C.

Equal temperature contour curves are shown, together with arrows showing the direction of falling temperature.   The highest melting salt, in this case KF, usually has the largest field and the ternary eutectic is closest

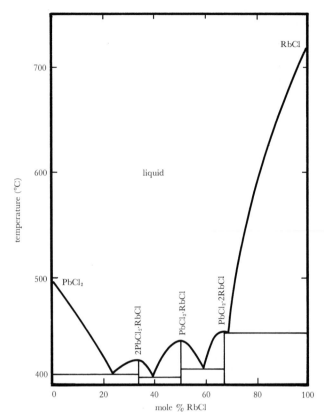

Fig. 4-5. *Phase diagram: PbCl₂ + RbCl system.* (*From data of K. Freis, Neues Jahrb. Mineral,* **37,** *766* (*1914*).)

to the three binary eutectics. Many ternary fluoride systems are of the simple eutectic type of Fig. 4-8.

When a liquid is cooled to the temperature of a contour, it forms, as the crystallization product, the pure solid in whose field the initial composition lies, leading to an equilibrium between solid and liquid at lower and lower temperature as more of the pure solid is precipitated, until the liquid composition reaches the relevant binary eutectic branch. The second solid of the binary eutectic then begins to be precipitated and the composition of the liquid changes in the direction of the ternary eutectic with decrease of temperature. When the temperature reaches that of the ternary eutectic E_4, an invariant temperature halt results as all three solids are precipitated until no further liquid remains.

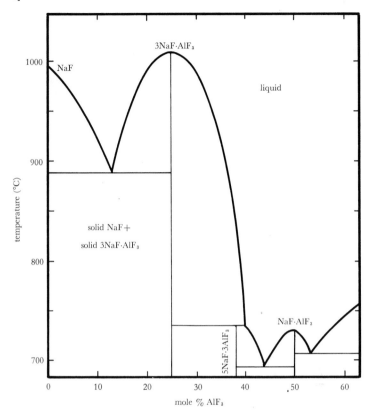

Fig. 4-6. *Phase diagram: NaF + AlF₃ system. (From L. M. Foster, Ann. N.Y. Acad. Sci.,* **79,** *919 (1960).)*

Polymorphic transitions of the solids, thermal decomposition of any component, and the formation of solid solutions necessitate further modification to the method of representation. A discussion of such systems is beyond the scope of this book.

Additive ternary systems forming one or more compounds. When one congruently melting compound is formed, this is equivalent to adding another pure solid to the system and a fourth field appears on the polythermal projection (i.e., the phase diagram). This is shown in Fig. 4-9 for the $Mg(NO_3)_2$ + KNO_3 + $NaNO_3$ system, where the congruently melting compound $2KNO_3 \cdot Mg(NO_3)_2$ is found with melting point 225°C. [$Mg(NO_3)_2$ decomposes above about 250°C; hence, its melting point is not given.] In this system there is a further complication in that $NaNO_3$ and KNO_3 form

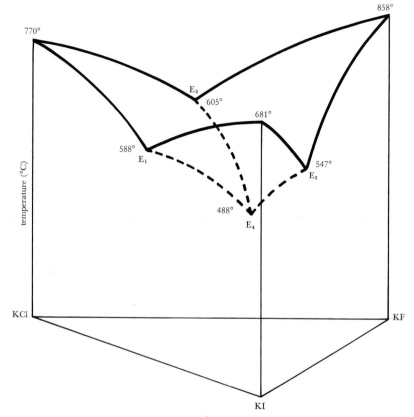

Fig. 4-7. *Phase diagram: Additive ternary system K / F, Cl, I (perspective). (From data of G. J. Nagornyj, Ann. Secteur Anal. Phys. Chem. USSR, **11**, 291 (1938).)*

solid solutions with a melting point minimum; hence, no binary eutectic is observed between them.

The system can be simplified, as in the case of a binary system with a congruently melting compound, by separation into two ternary systems, that is, $Mg(NO_3)_2 + NaNO_3 + 2KNO_3 \cdot Mg(NO_3)_2$ and $KNO_3 + NaNO_3 + 2KNO_3 \cdot Mg(NO_3)_2$. Each simple ternary system can now be considered in the same way as the $KF + KCl + KI$ system.

Additional modifications occur when more than one compound is formed and when incongruently melting compounds, polymorphic transitions, and so on are observed.

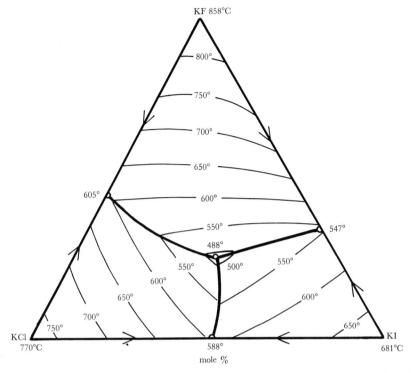

Fig. 4-8.   *Phase diagram: Additive ternary system K / F, Cl, I (polythermal projection).*
(From data of G. J. Nagornyj, Ann. Secteur Anal. Phys. Chem. USSR, **11,**
291 (1938).)

Reciprocal ternary systems.   Reciprocal salt systems are those for
which the pairs of salts have no ion in common and for which displacement
equilibria reactions can be written; for example

$$NaCl + KI \rightleftharpoons NaI + KCl$$

The composition of this system is usually written Na, K / Cl, I, and any
three binary salts can be taken as components.   Such a system requires four
composition axes for its representation and its polythermal projection is
shown in Fig. 4-10.   In a reciprocal ternary salt system two salts form a
stable pair depending on the Gibbs free energy change for the reaction; for
example, $(NX)_s + (MY)_s = (MX)_s + (NY)_s$.   If $-\Delta G$ for the forward
reaction is positive, then $(MX)_s$ and $(NY)_s$ are the stable pair and any mixture $NX + MY$ transforms to MX and NY completely, together with

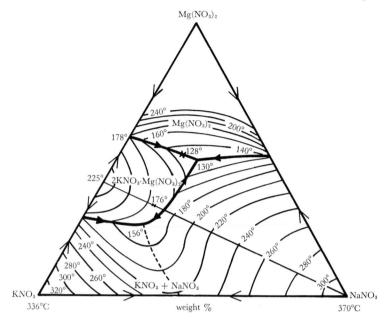

Fig. 4-9. *Phase diagram: Additive ternary system Na, K, Mg / NO₃. (From data of E. Jänecke, Z. Elektrochem., **48**, 454 (1942).)*

whichever of the original pair was taken in excess. The stable pair is triangulated at the temperature of solidification by the stable diagonal (shown as the unbroken line in Fig. 4-10).

In Na, K / Cl, I, the stable pair is NaCl + KI. The stable pair is given completely by solidification of the mixed vapor; that is, vapor consisting of NaI and KCl mixed together would give KI + NaCl on cooling. Between NaCl and KCl and NaI + KI, respectively, continuous series of solid solutions are formed. Between KCl and KI and NaCl and NaI, respectively, there are binary eutectics that vary in temperature with the composition of the liquid phases with which they are in equilibrium, as shown by the curves in Fig. 4-10. At the ternary eutectic (504°C) three solids will be formed on cooling. The saddle point 514°C along the stable diagonal is the eutectic for the quasi-binary system consisting of the stable pair.

The reciprocal system described above is of the simple type without compounds. Many variations are possible, including polymorphic transitions, unstable compounds, congruently and incongruently melting compounds, and others.

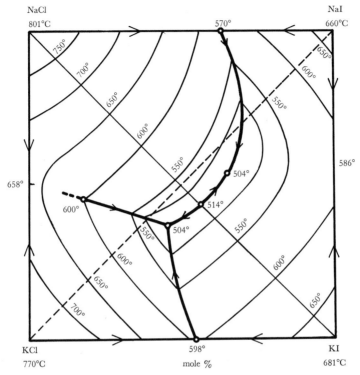

Fig. 4-10. *Phase diagram: Reciprocal ternary system Na, K / Cl, I. (From data of W. P. Radischtschew, J. Gen. Chem. USSR, **5**, 455 (1935).)*

4-4 ACTIVITY MODELS FOR MOLTEN SALT MIXTURES

The ideal solution thermodynamic relations of Section 4-1 apply without modification to many mixtures of simple species, such as monatomic substances or molecular compounds.   In the case of ionic salts dissolved in a neutral solvent, the ideal mixture laws apply to the limitingly dilute solutions.   As the dispersion of the ions by the neutral solvent leads to a random arrangement, entropy is calculated in the same way as for an ideal gas mixture.   For more concentrated solutions the activity coefficient is not unity.

For molten salts, the strong coulombic forces lead to the tendency for an alternation of charge, so that cations are surrounded by anions and vice versa. Hence the nonrandom arrangement leads to a configurational entropy contribution and the application of thermodynamics is dependent on a knowledge of this term.   Various models of molten salt mixtures have been proposed.

The basic model for calculating thermodynamic functions for molten salt mixtures is due to Temkin,[1] who considered salts to be completely ionized with the ions arranged in two interpenetrating quasi-lattices, one for cations and the other for the anions. The addition of another salt causes foreign cations to mix randomly with the original cations in the cation quasi-lattice and similarly for anions. The resulting entropy change can be deduced simply, using statistical mechanics, as

$$\Delta S_{\text{mix}} = -R(\Sigma n_i \ln x_i + \Sigma n_j \ln x_j) \qquad (4\text{-}24)$$

where n_i, n_j = number of moles of ions i^+, j^- and x_i, x_j are the mole fractions.

For a component of the mixture ij, the activity, using the Temkin ideal solution model, is given by

$$a_{ij} = x_i x_j \qquad (4\text{-}25)$$

If the solution contains only one anion, e.g., X^-, and a number of cations A^+, B^+, and so on, then for any component, e.g., AX, the mole fraction of X^-, $x_{X^-} = 1$, hence

$$a_{AX} = x_{A^+} = x_{AX} \qquad (4\text{-}26)$$

that is, the activity is the same as the mole fraction of the salt concerned. Similar reasoning applies when there is a common cation and different anions. For an ideal mixture of 1 mole of AX and 1 mole of AY, the activity of each salt is 0.5, but for 1 mole of AX with 1 mole of BY, the activity of each salt is 0.25.

For salts containing ions of the same number of charges, for example, A^+, B^+, X^-, Y^-, or A^{2+}, B^{2+}, X^{2-}, Y^{2-}, and so on, the ideal Temkin mixing model is applicable. For ions of different charges, however, such as the mixing of A^+, B^{2+}, X^-, there are difficulties in the derivation of an ideal solution law. For every B^{2+} ion added to the cation semilattice consisting of A^+ a hole must also be introduced, as electrically two A^+ are replaced for every B^{2+} added. The effect of the added hole on the entropy of mixing will depend on the concentration of holes already present. If AX is regarded as the solvent and BX_2 the solute, then the addition of BX_2, that is, the substitution of B^{2+} and a hole for two A^+, will have very little effect on the entropy of mixing provided that the concentration of holes in the solvent liquid is large enough. The ideal Temkin mixture law will then be followed. This is illustrated in Fig. 4-11 for the system $CdCl_2 + AgCl$ for which the activity of $CdCl_2$ is only slightly less than its mole fraction. Although experimental tests have not been made on many systems, it is clear from Chapter 2 that the large concentration of holes that X-ray diffraction and other studies indicate in molten salts makes it likely that the Temkin model will be basically applicable in binary salt systems, which are ideal. Other models, derived

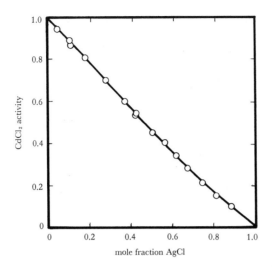

Fig. 4-11. *Activity of CdCl₂ at 1003°K in CdCl₂ + AgCl system.* (*From H. Bloom and B. J. Welch, Trans. Faraday Soc.*, **57**, *61* (*1961*).)

by Flood, Forland, and Grjotheim [2] and others, apply in special cases, e.g., for reciprocal systems.

For most systems, the almost ideal behavior shown by the $CdCl_2$ + $AgCl$ system does not apply, that is, activity coefficients deviate markedly from unity and deviations may be traced either to nonzero heats of mixing or to nonideal entropy due, for example, to the formation of complexes.

4-5 EMF OF MOLTEN SALT CONCENTRATION AND FORMATION CELLS

A satisfactory method of measuring activity in molten salt mixtures is by means of electromotive force determinations. For this purpose a formation cell of the type

$$Pb(l)|PbCl_2 + MCl(l)|Cl_2(g)|C \qquad (A)$$

can be used. This is shown diagrammatically in Fig. 4-12. Chlorine is passed over a graphite rod through holes in a glass sheath into the melt to form the chlorine electrode. The molten lead electrode is formed within a glass tube containing melt of the same composition and connected with the bulk melt of the same composition via a sintered glass disk. The electrode connections to the potentiometer are by means of high melting, for example, tungsten wires from the carbon rod and (sheathed in glass to prevent electrical contact with the melt) from the molten lead pool. The thermo-emf of the

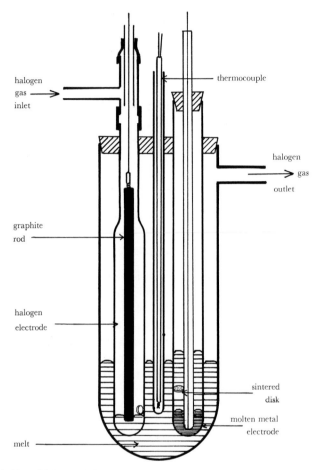

Fig. 4-12. *Molten salt formation cell for emf measurements.*

tungsten–graphite thermocouple must be taken into account, as this is super-imposed on the emf of the cell.

The electrode reactions in the formation cell (A) are, at the lead electrode,

$$\cdot \, \mathrm{Pb}(l) \rightarrow \mathrm{Pb^{2+}} + 2e^- \quad \text{(anode)}$$

and at the chlorine electrode,

$$\mathrm{Cl_2}(g) + 2e^- \rightarrow 2\mathrm{Cl^-} \quad \text{(cathode)}.$$

The cell is thus a formation cell with $\mathrm{PbCl_2}$ being produced from its elements in the solution of $\mathrm{PbCl_2}$ in MCl. If $a_{\mathrm{PbCl_2}}$ is the activity of $\mathrm{PbCl_2}$ in the melt, the emf $\mathcal{E}$ of the cell will be given by

$$\mathcal{E} = \mathcal{E}^0 - \frac{RT}{z\mathfrak{F}} \ln a_{\mathrm{PbCl_2}} \tag{4-27}$$

where z electrons are involved in the cell reaction and $\mathfrak{F}$ is the faraday. The value of $\mathcal{E}^0$ (i.e., the standard emf of the cell) is obtained by measuring the emf of the formation cell using pure $\mathrm{PbCl_2}$ as the electrolyte, that is, with $a_{\mathrm{PbCl_2}} = 1$. Cells as shown in Fig. 4-12 can be used for determining activities and other thermodynamic quantities in molten salts and owe their origin to the investigations of Hildebrand and Salstrom.[3]

Other types of cells used for emf measurements involve a liquid junction, for example

$$\mathrm{Pb | molten\ PbCl_2 \| molten\ CdCl_2 | Cd} \tag{B}$$

and

$$\mathrm{Pb | PbCl_2 + MCl}(l) \| \mathrm{pure\ PbCl_2 | Pb} \tag{C}$$

Both the Daniell cell (B) and the concentration cell (C) have been investigated but cannot be used directly for the calculation of thermodynamic data owing to the diffusion potentials at the liquid junctions. For this reason also the use of reference electrodes to establish relative electrode potentials is somewhat arbitrary. Formation cells of type (A) only are capable of producing accurate thermodynamic information. The combination of two formation cells, with different melt compositions, produces a concentration cell without liquid junction.

For the cell

$$\mathrm{A}(l) | \underset{x_{\mathrm{AX_2}}}{\mathrm{AX_2}(l)} + \underset{x_{\mathrm{MX}}}{\mathrm{MX}(l)} | \mathrm{X_2}(g),\ \mathrm{C} \tag{D}$$

where $\mathrm{AX_2}$ could represent $\mathrm{PbCl_2}$ as in (A) and M could be an alkali metal, its emf is that of the formation cell for the production of $\mathrm{AX_2}$ from its elements at mole fraction $x_{\mathrm{AX_2}}$, in a solvent MX of mole fraction $x_{\mathrm{MX}} \cdot (x_{\mathrm{AX_2}} + x_{\mathrm{MX}} = 1)$.

The standard free energy of formation of $\mathrm{AX_2}$ at the temperature of measurement is given by

$$\Delta G^0_{\mathrm{AX_2}} = -z\mathfrak{F}\mathcal{E}^0 \tag{4-28}$$

and the standard entropy of formation

$$\Delta S^0_{\mathrm{AX_2}} = z\mathfrak{F} \frac{d\mathcal{E}^0}{dT} \tag{4-29}$$

The standard heat of formation is

$$\Delta H^0_{\mathrm{AX_2}} = z\mathfrak{F} \left(T \frac{d\mathcal{E}^0}{dT} - \mathcal{E}^0 \right) \tag{4-30}$$

Equations (4-28), (4-29), and (4-30) apply to the cell (D), where $x_{AX_2} = 1$, that is, for the pure electrolyte in its standard state.

For other than the pure electrolyte, that is, when x_{AX_2} is not equal to unity, we have

$$\Delta G_{AX_2} = -z\mathfrak{F}\mathcal{E} \tag{4-31}$$

$$\Delta S_{AX_2} = z\mathfrak{F}\left(\frac{d\mathcal{E}}{dT}\right) \tag{4-32}$$

$$\Delta H_{AX_2} = z\mathfrak{F}\left(T\frac{d\mathcal{E}}{dT} - \mathcal{E}\right) \tag{4-33}$$

The quantities ΔG_{AX_2}, ΔS_{AX_2}, and ΔH_{AX_2} now refer to the formation of 1 mole of AX_2 in the mixture. Hence $\Delta G_{AX_2} - \Delta G_{AX_2}^0$, etc., represent the change of thermodynamic quantity resulting from the transfer of 1 mole of AX_2 from its standard state (the pure liquid) to a solution in which its mole fraction is x_{AX_2} at the same temperature. Thus the partial molar thermodynamic quantities can be obtained by measurement of $\mathcal{E}$, $\mathcal{E}^0$, and their temperature coefficients, as follows.

$$\Delta \bar{G}_{AX_2} = \Delta G_{AX_2} - \Delta G_{AX_2}^0 = -z\mathfrak{F}(\mathcal{E} - \mathcal{E}^0)$$
$$= RT \ln a_{AX_2} \tag{4-34}$$

$$\Delta \bar{S}_{AX_2} = \Delta S_{AX_2} - \Delta S_{AX_2}^0$$
$$= z\mathfrak{F}\left(\frac{d\mathcal{E}}{dT} - \frac{d\mathcal{E}^0}{dT}\right) \tag{4-35}$$

$$\Delta \bar{H}_{AX_2} = \Delta H_{AX_2} - \Delta H_{AX_2}^0$$
$$= \Delta \bar{G}_{AX_2} + T\Delta \bar{S}_{AX_2}$$
$$= -z\mathfrak{F}(\mathcal{E} - \mathcal{E}^0) + Tz\mathfrak{F}\left(\frac{d\mathcal{E}}{dT} - \frac{d\mathcal{E}^0}{dT}\right) \tag{4-36}$$

If the components of the mixture form an ideal solution

$$\Delta \bar{G}_{AX_2} \text{ (ideal)} = RT \ln x_{AX_2} \tag{4-37}$$
$$\Delta \bar{S}_{AX_2} \text{ (ideal)} = -R \ln x_{AX_2} \tag{4-38}$$
$$\Delta \bar{H}_{AX_2} \text{ (ideal)} = 0 \tag{4-39}$$

The differences, actual partial molar thermodynamic quantity minus ideal partial thermodynamic quantity, are the excess partial thermodynamic quantities, $\bar{G}^E$, $\bar{H}^E$, and $\bar{S}^E$, which give a measure of the deviations from ideal behavior. Thus

$$\bar{G}_{AX_2}^E = -z\mathfrak{F}(\mathcal{E} - \mathcal{E}^0) - RT \ln x_{AX_2} = RT \ln \gamma_{AX_2} \tag{4-40}$$

from which activity coefficients can be determined. The equation for $\bar{S}_{AX_2}^E$ can also be expressed in terms of $\mathcal{E}$ and $\mathcal{E}^0$ by combining Eqs. (4-35) and

(4-38).   From (4-39) it is clear that in (4-36) $\bar{H}_{AX_2}^E$ can be substituted for $\Delta \bar{H}_{AX_2}$.

Calculation of the Integral Thermodynamic Quantities

Electromotive force determinations from a particular galvanic cell give only the partial thermodynamic data relating to one component of the mixture.   The thermodynamic data pertaining to the other component of a binary mixture and the integral thermodynamic quantities of mixing can be obtained readily; for example, from the equation for the free energy of mixing, per mole, for components 1 (mole fraction x_1) and 2 (mole fraction x_2)

$$\Delta G_{mix} = x_1 \Delta \bar{G}_1 + x_2 \Delta \bar{G}_2 \qquad (\text{where } x_2 = 1 - x_1) \qquad (4\text{-}41)$$

it can be shown readily that

$$\Delta G_{mix} = (1 - x_1) \int_{x_1=0}^{x_1} \frac{\Delta \bar{G}_1}{(1 - x_1)^2} \, dx_1 \qquad (4\text{-}42)$$

Thus the free energy of mixing of x_1 moles of component 1 and $(1 - x_1)$ moles of component 2, that is, ΔG_{mix}, can be computed by plotting $\Delta \bar{G}_1/(1 - x_1)^2$ as ordinate against mole fraction of component 1 and graphically integrating by determination of area under the curve between 0 and x_1. $\Delta \bar{G}_2$ can then be determined from ΔG_{mix} and $\Delta \bar{G}_1$ by using Eq. (4-41).

Equations analogous to (4-42) apply for the heat and entropy of mixing; that is,

$$\Delta H_{mix} = (1 - x_1) \int_{x_1=0}^{x_1} \frac{\Delta \bar{H}_1}{(1 - x_1)^2} \, dx_1 \qquad (4\text{-}43)$$

$$\Delta S_{mix} = (1 - x_1) \int_{x_1=0}^{x_1} \frac{\Delta \bar{S}_1}{(1 - x_1)^2} \, dx_1 \qquad (4\text{-}44)$$

An alternative method of calculating $\Delta \bar{G}_2$, etc., from $\Delta \bar{G}_1$, etc., is to integrate the Gibbs-Duhem expression (4-8) in the form

$$d\bar{G}_2 = -\frac{x_1}{x_2} d\bar{G}_1 \qquad (4\text{-}45)$$

To aid evaluation, activities or activity coefficients are used instead of partial molar free energies, and the equation

$$\log \gamma_2 = - \int_{x_1=0}^{x_1} \frac{x_1}{x_2} d \log \gamma_1 \qquad (4\text{-}46)$$

results.   To evaluate (4-46), x_1/x_2 is plotted against $\log \gamma_1$, and the area under the curve from 0 to x_1 is obtained by graphical summation. ΔG_{mix} can then be obtained by using Eq. (4-41).   Equation (4-46) also allows calculation of the activity of one component of a binary mixture when that of the other component is known.

4-6 VAPOR PRESSURE OF MOLTEN HALIDE SYSTEMS

For the determination of thermodynamic activity in mixtures of molten salts, vapor pressure measurements have also been widely used. They can be classified into two categories, absolute and nonabsolute. Absolute methods do not require the use of the gas law for calculation of vapor pressure. Nonabsolute methods require the use of the gas law and must make an assumption respecting the molecular weight of the salt vapor. Alternatively, an absolute method may be used to determine the vapor pressure, which can then be used in conjunction with a nonabsolute method to determine molecular weight of the vapor.

Absolute Methods

Most classical methods have been used. Among the most useful for salt vapors is direct manometric measurement with the use of a Bourdon (spoon or sickle) gage as a null detector.

Boiling and dew point methods. Condensation of $ZrCl_4$ above molten mixtures of $ZrCl_4$ + $NaCl$ and $ZrCl_4$ + KCl has been used to determine vapor pressure by the dew point method.

The most accurate absolute method is the determination of boiling point at pressures that are held constant at various values between a few millimeters of Hg and 1 atm. The method was originated by Ruff and Bergdahl (1919) and was used in many early vapor pressure studies but the results were often uncertain due to superheating (up to 20°C). Barton and Bloom [4] found that the introduction of a slow stream of N_2 or Ar prevents superheating. Their apparatus is shown diagrammatically in Fig. 4-13.

The melt is held in a silica boiling tube in which is situated a silica "cold finger" condenser (cooled by compressed air). The temperature of boiling is determined by means of a noble metal thermocouple with the hot junction situated close to the surface of the melt to eliminate errors due to increase of measured temperature with increase of pressure (i.e., with depth of immersion). Experimentally the method is very straightforward. The temperature of the surrounding furnace as measured by another thermocouple is initially lower than the boiling point at the particular constant pressure which is applied and kept constant by means of a manostat. The furnace is allowed to heat slowly, the boiling point being the constant temperature registered by the thermocouple at the surface of the melt while the thermocouple that registers furnace temperature continues to rise steadily. Pressure is measured by means of a manometer. The experiment is repeated at

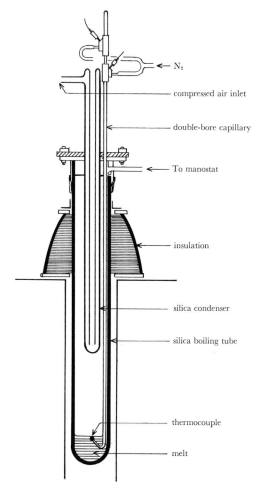

← N₂

compressed air inlet

double-bore capillary

← To manostat

insulation

silica condenser

silica boiling tube

thermocouple

melt

Fig. 4-13. *Vapor pressure determination by measurement of boiling point.*

various pressures, giving variation of boiling point with pressure. This method can be used to determine vapor pressure of a pure salt and total vapor pressure of a mixture.

Nonabsolute Methods

Transpiration. This method is the most widely used indirect method and its use in molten salt systems originated with Rosner and Jellinek.[5] A typical apparatus is shown in Fig. 4-14.

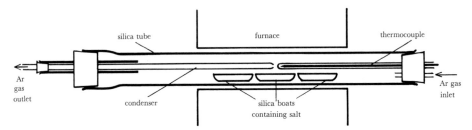

Fig. 4-14. *Determination of vapor pressure by transpiration.*

An inert gas, such as Ar, is passed over silica boats containing the molten salt, becomes saturated with vapor, and enters a silica condenser tube situated very close to the thermocouple used for measuring temperature. The salt vapor condenses in the silica tube while the inert gas passes through to be collected and its volume measured. The weight of salt vapor collected is determined by analysis of the condenser contents. By assuming that the ideal gas law is obeyed (found to be a reasonable assumption at pressure below atmospheric), vapor pressure can be calculated if the molecular weight is known. Assumption that molecular weight is the same as formula weight is often made but is usually incorrect owing to polymerization of the vapor (see Chapter 7). The main advantage of the transpiration method is that it can be used to determine the partial pressures of components of a mixture.

Effusion. For high melting substances vapor pressure can be determined by Knudsen's formulas from weight of substance escaping into a vacuum from a small hole in a box.

Thermodynamic Data from Vapor Pressure

Equation (4-4) is used to determine the activity of the component of a mixture for which vapor pressure has been obtained.

For a binary salt system with one volatile component at a suitable temperature, for example, $PbCl_2$ in $PbCl_2 + CsCl$, the thermodynamic properties of the nonvolatile component (i.e., $CsCl$) can be calculated by using graphical integration procedures as outlined under Section 4-5. Activity values from careful vapor pressure measurements agree well with those determined by emf methods (Section 4-5). It is necessary, however, to take into account intermolecular compounds in the vapor when calculating activity from vapor pressure. This will be discussed further in Chapter 7.

4-7 CRYOSCOPY

Depression of the freezing point of one salt (the "solvent") by addition of the other (the "solute") has been used to determine thermodynamic information on molten salt mixtures.

Taking any simple binary system, such as $PbCl_2 + NaCl$ (Fig. 4-1), in which solid solutions are not formed—that is, for which the pure solvent salt is deposited on cooling the melt—the thermodynamic quantities for fusion are related as follows:

$$\Delta G_{f(T)} = \Delta H_{f(T)} - T\Delta S_{f(T)} \tag{4-47}$$

$\Delta H_{f(T)}$, $\Delta G_{f(T)}$, and $\Delta S_{f(T)}$ are heat, free energy, and entropy, respectively, for fusion of the solvent at temperature T (i.e., the temperature of first separation of solvent on cooling the solution). These quantities are in general not the same as the quantities ΔH_f^0, ΔG_f^0, and ΔS_f^0 for the pure solvent at its melting point T^0. $\Delta H_{f(T)}$ is related to ΔH_f^0 as follows:

$$\Delta H_{f(T)} = \Delta H_f^0 + \int_{T^0}^{T} \Delta C_p \, dT \tag{4-48}$$

where $\Delta C_p = C_p$ (liquid) $- C_p$ (solid).

The activity a_s of the solvent at temperature T can be deduced simply for the mixture as

$$\ln a_{s(T)} = \frac{-\Delta H_f^0}{R}\left(\frac{1}{T} - \frac{1}{T^0}\right) - \frac{\Delta C_p}{R}\left[\ln\left(\frac{T^0}{T}\right) - \frac{T^0 - T}{T}\right] \tag{4-49}$$

Thus the measured freezing point depression of the solvent and the necessary calorimetric data enable the accurate calculation of activity of solvent at temperature T by means of Eq. (4-49).

If heat capacity data are not available, the ΔC_p term in Eq. (4-49) is ignored, giving

$$\ln a_{s(T)} = \frac{-\Delta H_f^0}{R}\left(\frac{1}{T} - \frac{1}{T^0}\right) \tag{4-50}$$

leading to results that do not differ much from those of (4-49). The activity data for any particular system will be over a range of temperatures but can be recalculated at a constant temperature by assuming that the solutions are regular and using Eq. (4-22) thus

$$\ln a_{s(T_2)} = \left(\frac{T_1}{T_2}\right)\ln a_{s(T_1)} + \frac{T_2 - T_1}{T_2}\ln x_s \tag{4-51}$$

The change of activity with temperature is usually very small according to Eq. (4-51) and this is in accord with other methods of measurement.

For very dilute solutions, Eq. (4-50) can be readily rearranged to give the lowering of the freezing point

$$(T^0 - T) = \frac{\nu_i R (T_f{}^0)^2}{\Delta H_f{}^0} x = k\nu_i x \qquad (4\text{-}52)$$

which is the Raoult-van't Hoff freezing point depression law. ν_i is the number of ions given per molecule of salt, and only ions that are not in common with those of the solvent salt are relevant in producing a freezing point depression; x is the mole fraction of solute.

From (4-52) it is clear that freezing point depression is proportional to mole fraction of solute (for dilute solutions) and that the constant of proportionality depends on the number of ions of solute salt not common with the solvent salt. This behavior is illustrated in Fig. 4-15 relating to freezing point of $AgNO_3$ as solvent (Kordes et al.[6]). For the solutes Ag_2SO_4 and $Pb(NO_3)_2$, each with one ion in common with the solvent, a unit slope freezing point depression line is produced. $ZnSO_4$, $PbSO_4$, and $KClO_4$ give

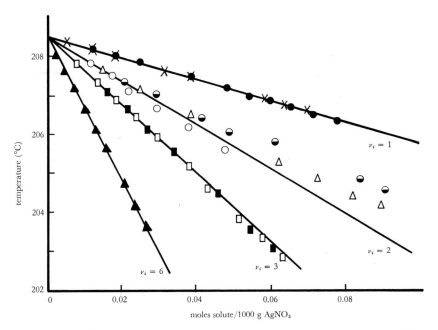

Fig. 4-15. *Freezing point depressions in the solvent silver nitrate. Experimental points:* $\times$, Ag_2SO_4; $\bullet$, $Pb(NO_3)_2$; $\ominus$, $ZnSO_4$; $\bigcirc$, $PbSO_4$; $\triangle$, $KClO_4$; $\blacksquare$, $K_2Cr_2O_7$; $\square$, $PbCl_2$; $\blacktriangle$, $K_2[Hg(Cr_2O_7)Cl_2]$. *Theoretical lines for* $\nu_i = 1, 2, 3,$ *and 6 are shown.* (*From Kordes et al.*[6])

twice the depression, while for $K_2Cr_2O_7$ and $PbCl_2$, each with 3 ions not common to the solvent, a threefold depression is produced. $K_2[Hg(Cr_2O_7)Cl_2]$ gives a sixfold depression.

The departure from linearity with increase of concentration is noticeable particularly for $ZnSO_4$ and $KClO_4$ as solutes. This is to be expected, as (4-52) is only strictly applicable to very dilute solutions.

The cryoscopic method is most apt for demonstrating the ionic nature of molten salts and can be used to assist in the establishment of formulas of complex ions.

4-8 HEAT CAPACITY OF MOLTEN SALTS—HEAT AND ENTROPY OF MIXING

Calorimetric investigations of molten salt systems have been carried out extensively by Kleppa and co-workers,[7] who developed a twin differential reaction calorimeter capable of measuring heat of mixing accurately below 500°C and with less accuracy as high as 800°C.

This is illustrated in Fig. 4-16. Two nearly identical differential calorimeters are located in cylindrical wells in a heavy aluminum jacket. In each of the twin units a temperature difference between the calorimeter and the surrounding jacket gives rise to a thermo-emf in a 96-junction thermopile. The two thermopiles are connected in series in such a manner that the emf of one thermopile opposes that of the other. Hence small drifts in temperature of the aluminum jacket will affect both emf's similarly but in the opposite sense, thus allowing an accurate determination of any very small temperature difference between the two calorimeters.

The whole assembly is heated to the required temperature. As long as no heat is generated in one or other calorimeter, the difference emf remains zero. For carrying out a determination of enthalpy of mixing, known quantities of molten salt are mixed directly in one of the calorimeters— the other serves as a reference. The apparatus can be calibrated to determine heat of mixing directly from the temperature difference between the calorimeters after mixing. The experimental error of this method can be as low as $\pm 0.5\%$.

Various other investigators have used other methods. Bloom and Tricklebank[8] used a Bunsen fusion calorimeter to investigate enthalpy change on cooling molten salt mixtures from known temperatures in excess of 800°C to room temperature. From heat evolved on cooling from a number of different temperatures to the fixed lower temperature, heat capacity of molten salts and their mixtures are readily calculated by this method, as are heats and entropies of transitions, e.g., freezing, in the temperature range under investigation. The enthalpies of mixing of molten salts can be calcu-

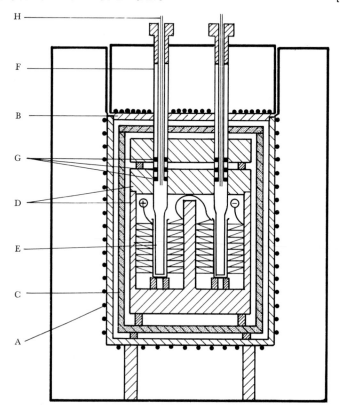

Fig. 4-16. *Twin calorimeter for measurement of heats of mixing of molten salts. A, main heater; B, top heater; C, heavy shield; D, aluminum jacket; E, calorimeter; F, protection tube; G, radiation shields; H, manipulation tube;* $\oplus$——$\ominus$, *thermopile (from Kleppa* [7]*).*

lated also, knowing the enthalpies of cooling the mixture and the pure components to the fixed lower temperature, together with the heat of formation of
the solid mixture (determined separately by solution calorimetry).

The direct mixing method of Kleppa is preferable except when a
volatile salt is concerned, in which case the direct mixing method is subject
to errors due to the heat of vaporization, this shortcoming is avoided in the
drop method by the use of sealed capsules.

For alkali nitrate + chloride and alkali nitrate + bromide mixtures,
the enthalpies of mixing are small and positive, the largest values being for
the sodium systems and decreasing in the sequence $Na^+ > K^+ > Rb^+ > Cs^+$,
whereas some binary systems, e.g., $NaNO_3 + KNO_3$, have small negative

enthalpies of mixing.   These relatively small heat effects have been explained in terms of mainly physical forces of interaction between ions on mixing.

Kleppa and co-workers [7] have utilized various empirical and semi-empirical expressions to obtain a relation between compositions and the enthalpy of mixing per mole for molten salt systems.   Their earlier results were expressed in the form

$$\Delta H_{\text{mix}} = x(1 - x)[a + bx + cx(1 - x)] \qquad (4\text{-}53)$$

where x is the mole fraction of the salt with the smaller cation.   For any given system, a, b, c are constants.

Theories of charge symmetrical molten salt mixtures, e.g., binary alkali nitrates, have been developed on the basis of a modified conformal solution theory that relates heat of mixing with ionic dimensions and interionic forces of interaction.   The extension of the theory by Davis and Rice [9] gives rise to the expression

$$\Delta H_{\text{mix}} = x(1 - x)(U_0 + U_1 \delta_{12} + U_2 \delta_{12}^2) \qquad (4\text{-}54)$$

In Eq. (4-54)

$$\delta_{12} = \frac{(d_1 - d_2)}{d_1 d_2} \qquad (4\text{-}55)$$

where d_1 and d_2 are the sums of the ionic radii of the two component salts, respectively. U_0, U_1, and U_2 are unevaluated coefficients that may be described qualitatively in terms of the type of interactions on which they depend.

The enthalpies of mixing per mole for all the binary alkali halide systems can be represented approximately by the expression

$$\Delta H_{\text{mix}} = x(1 - x)(U_0^{++} - 340\delta_{12}^2) \qquad \text{kcal mole}^{-1} \qquad (4\text{-}56)$$

The final term on the right-hand side corresponds to the term $U_2 \delta_{12}^2$ in Eq. (4-54) and the $U_1 \delta_{12}$ term of this equation is not applicable.   For the silver chloride + alkali chloride and thallium chloride + alkali chloride liquid systems, however, the enthalpy of mixing equations require the inclusion of the $U_1 \delta_{12}$ term.

For many molten salt systems, mixing involves the evolution of considerable heat, for example, for the $MgCl_2$ + alkali chloride systems investigated by Kleppa and McCarty,[10] ΔH_{mix} is negative and $-\Delta H_{\text{mix}}$ increases sharply in the sequence Li < Na < K < Rb < Cs.   The results are shown in Fig. 4-17 and it can be seen that the maximum in negative enthalpy is in excess of 5 kcal mole^{-1} for the $MgCl_2$ + CsCl system at 730°C at a composition slightly more than 0.6 mole fraction CsCl.   The results can be explained by the formation of the complex anionic species $MgCl_4^{2-}$ whose stability

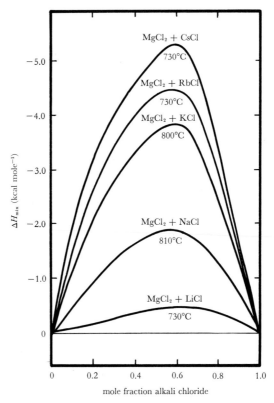

Fig. 4-17. *Heat of mixing of molten MgCl₂ with molten alkali chlorides (from Kleppa and McCarty [10]).*

depends strongly on the alkali cation present, and increases from Li^+ to Cs^+. This will be discussed further in Section 4-12.

For mixtures of $MgCl_2$ with NaCl, KCl, RbCl, and CsCl, respectively, Kleppa and McCarty showed that ΔH_{mix} changes linearly with the parameter δ_{12}. This is consistent with the application of conformal solution theory to charge unsymmetrical systems.

4-9 COMPRESSIBILITY

The compressibilities of many molten salts have been measured by Bockris and co-workers [11] by determination of the velocity of ultrasonic mechanical vibrations of about 10^6 cycle sec^{-1} in the melt. The velocity of ultrasound U_L in these liquids was found to be strictly proportional to the square root of absolute temperature, but over a temperature range of 200°–

$500°C$ a linear relation with absolute temperature is applicable; that is,

$$U_L = U_0 - aT \qquad (4\text{-}57)$$

where U_0 and a are constants.

Some values of these constants are given in Table 4-2 (Bockris and Richards [11]).

Thus the velocity of ultrasound in molten salts is of the same order of magnitude as in room temperature liquids.

The values of the isothermal compressibility β_T, the adiabatic compressibility β_S, and γ (i.e., C_p/C_v) can be obtained from values of U_L by means of the thermodynamic equations

$$\beta_T = \gamma\beta_S = \frac{\gamma V}{U_L^2 M} \qquad (4\text{-}58)$$

and

$$\gamma - 1 = \frac{U_L^2 \alpha^2 TM}{C_p} \qquad (4\text{-}59)$$

where α = coefficient of thermal expansion (or expansivity) and M is the formula weight.

The isothermal compressibility values for molten salts increase with increasing temperature, and vary between about 20×10^{-12} and 100×10^{-12} cm^2 dyne^{-1} for the molten group I halides. The compressibility and derived thermodynamic data have been used by Bockris and Richards to test structural models for molten salts.

4-10 DENSITY AND MOLAR VOLUME

Density of a molten salt is measured by methods essentially similar to those for room temperature liquids and may be divided into Archimedean and pyknometric methods.

Table 4-2 *Ultrasonic Velocities in Molten Salts*

Salt	U_0 (m sec^{-1})	a (m sec^{-1} °C^{-1})	Temperature range (°C)
LiCl	2556	0.849	620–1010
NaCl	2483	0.915	810–1010
KCl	2275	0.878	785–1020
CsCl	1597	0.675	660–1010

Most methods (see, e.g., Bloom *et al.*[12]) based on the principle of Archimedes compare the loss in weight of a noble metal (usually 1–1.5 cm³ Pt or Pt + Rh) sinker (or bob) when immersed in the molten salt, which is held at a constant temperature in an electric furnace, with the weight lost when the sinker is immersed in a calibrating liquid. The balance is rigidly supported on a suitable table above the furnace. Water at a known temperature is the usual calibrating liquid.

Corrections must be applied for expansion of the sinker from temperature of calibrating liquid to temperature of the melt; also for the upward pull due to surface tension of the melt on the platinum wire supporting the sinker. Correction for buoyancy of the sinker in air is also often applied. Care must be taken to prevent condensation of volatile constituents of the melt on the supporting wire. An accuracy of $\pm 0.1\%$ may be achieved.

For volatile salts, pyknometer or dilatometer methods are preferable; for example, the salt may be introduced into a silica dilatometer bulb that is suspended in a furnace with a viewing window through which the level of the melt in the narrow stem can be compared with graduations by means of a cathetometer. The dilatometer is calibrated at room temperature by means of water or another suitable liquid. Pyknometers of metal or other high melting materials, which can be filled to a given volume and weighed after cooling, are also used. The accuracy of these methods is also of the order of $\pm 0.1\%$.

Molar volume of the pure molten salt V^0 can be calculated from the measured density d^0 by the equation

$$V^0 = \frac{M}{d^0} \tag{4-60}$$

Comparisons of physical properties such as molar volume are made difficult for different molten salts by the large range of melting points. Various investigators have suggested different methods of comparison based on the concept of *corresponding temperatures*. Suitable temperatures for comparison of different molten salts are 10% in degrees absolute above the melting point, i.e., 1.1 T_{fus}, as at that stage any residual effects due to postmelting phenomena will probably have been overcome. Table 4-3 gives the molar volumes of a number of molten salts at 1.1 T_{fus}. It can be seen that molar volume increases progressively from LiCl to CsCl in the same direction as increase of cation radius.

For a mixture of molten salts of density d, molar volume V is given by

$$V = \frac{\Sigma_i(x_i M_i)}{d} \tag{4-61}$$

Table 4-3   *Molar Volume at 10%*
above m.p. for Pure Molten Salts [a]

Salt	m.p. (°K)	V^0 (ml)
LiCl	883	28.96
NaCl	1074	39.02
KCl	1043	50.82
RbCl	995	56.10
CsCl	918	62.53
$ZnCl_2$	591	54.68
$CdCl_2$	841	55.24
$PbCl_2$	773	57.54

[a] That is, at 1.1 T_{fus}.

and the excess volume per mole on mixing ΔV^E by

$$\Delta V^E = \frac{\Sigma_i(x_i M_i)}{d} - \Sigma_i(x_i V_i^0) \qquad (4\text{-}62)$$

Ideal Molten Salt Systems

Figure 4-18 illustrates the linear molar volume isotherms for a number of molten salt systems for which $\Delta V^E = 0$. For such systems other physical properties as well as molar volume indicate that random mixing takes place without formation of associated species such as complex ions. They include the systems $CdCl_2 + CdBr_2$, $PbCl_2 + PbBr_2$, $PbCl_2 + AgCl$, and $AgCl + AgBr$ (all investigated by Boardman, Dorman, and Heymann [13]). For the $PbCl_2 + CdCl_2$ system ΔV^E has negative values (ΔV^E reaches -0.84% of V at approximately 0.67 mole fraction $PbCl_2$ at 600°C). The reason for this is not understood but the system is known to be ideal on the basis of other physical measurements. A few other systems have negative ΔV^E values.

Nonideal Molten Salt Systems

For the $PbCl_2 + MCl$ systems (M = Li, Na, K, Rb, Cs) the values of ΔV^E at 0.5 mole fraction $PbCl_2$ change progressively from $\Delta V^E = 0$ for M = Li, to $\Delta V^E = +2.5$ ml (at 720°C) for M = Cs. This represents an expansion of approximately 4.1% greater than ideal mixing (at 0.5 mole fraction CsCl). The molar volumes at 720°C are shown for $PbCl_2 + NaCl$, $PbCl_2 + KCl$, $PbCl_2 + RbCl$, and $PbCl_2 + CsCl$ in Fig. 4-19. The effects are similar for the $CdCl_2 + MCl$ systems and have been attributed to the

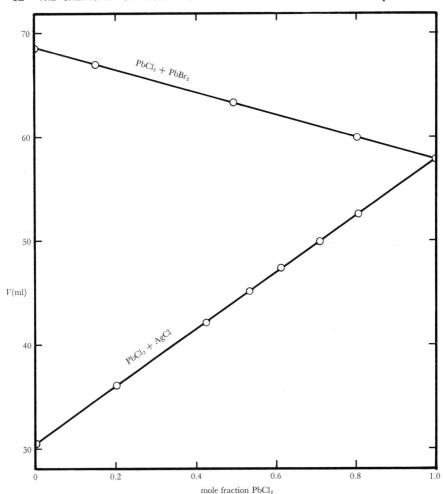

Fig. 4-18.   *Molar volume isotherms at 600°C for the PbCl₂ + PbBr₂ and PbCl₂ + AgCl systems (from the results of Boardman et al.[13]).*

progressive increase in the formation of complex ionic species from Li through to Cs (see Section 4-12).

Partial Molar Volume and Expansibility

The partial molar volumes of constituents of molten salt mixtures, particularly silicate systems, have been used to gain useful structural information.

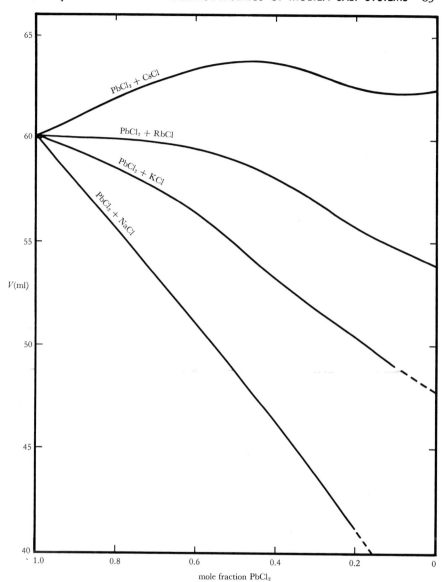

Fig. 4-19. *Molar volume isotherms at 720°C for $PbCl_2 + MCl$ systems ($M =$ Cs, Rb, K, Na) (from Bloom et al.[12]).*

For a system of two components

$$\bar{V}_1 = \left(\frac{\partial V}{\partial x_1}\right)_{x_2,T,P} \qquad \bar{V}_2 = \left(\frac{\partial V}{\partial x_2}\right)_{x_1,T,P} \qquad (4\text{-}63)$$

$\bar{V}_1$ and $\bar{V}_2$ are obtained readily from molar volume isotherms by means of the graphical method of intercepts; for example, at a particular mole fraction x_1 the intercept that the tangent to the molar volume curve makes with the $x_1 = 1$ ordinate gives $\bar{V}_1$ and the intercept with the $x_2 = 1$ ordinate gives $\bar{V}_2$. The molar volume is given by

$$V = \Sigma(x_i\bar{V}_i) \qquad (4\text{-}64)$$

The molar expansibility $(\partial V/\partial T)_P$ is related to expansivity α by

$$\left(\frac{\partial V}{\partial T}\right)_P = V\alpha = -\frac{V}{d}\left(\frac{\partial d}{\partial T}\right)_P \qquad (4\text{-}65)$$

and is of considerable value in the investigation of structure of molten silicates.

4-11 THE THERMODYNAMICS OF RECIPROCAL MOLTEN SALT SYSTEMS

In reciprocal molten salt systems such as Na^+, K^+ / Cl^-, I^-, free energy changes accompany the formation of the solution, as discussed in Section 4-4. For the reaction of pure NaI and pure KCl to form the mixture the equilibrium is

$$NaI + KCl = NaCl + KI$$

for which the standard Gibbs free energy increase is ΔG^0. For such a system, the entropy of random mixing is given by

$$\Delta S_{mix} = -n R(x_{Na^+} \cdot \ln x_{Na^+} + x_{K^+} \cdot \ln x_{K^+}) - n R(x_{Cl^-} \cdot \ln x_{Cl^-} + x_{I^-} \cdot \ln x_{I^-}) \qquad (4\text{-}66)$$

where n is the total number of cations or anions in moles and x is the respective ionic fraction.

The partial molar entropy of mixing of one component, e.g., NaI, is obtained by differentiating with respect to its number of moles, n_{NaI}

$$(dn_{NaI} = dn_{Na^+} = dn_{I^-})$$

Hence

$$\Delta \bar{S}_{NaI} = \frac{\partial \Delta S_{mix}}{\partial n_{NaI}} - R x_{Na^+} \cdot x_{I^-} \qquad (4\text{-}67)$$

If $\bar{G}^0_{NaI}$, etc., represents the standard partial molar free energy of each component of the mixture, it follows that

$$\bar{G}^0_{NaCl} + \bar{G}^0_{KI} - \bar{G}^0_{NaI} - \bar{G}^0_{KCl} = \Delta G^0 \qquad (4\text{-}68)$$

As the pure component constitutes the standard state, the partial molar free energy of a particular component of the mixture, e.g., NaI, is

$$\Delta \bar{G}_{NaI} = \bar{G}_{NaI} - \bar{G}^0_{NaI} \qquad (4\text{-}69)$$

Equation (4-69) allows calculation of activity and activity coefficient of a particular component as, utilizing Eq. (4-17),

$$RT \ln a_{NaI} = \Delta \bar{G}_{NaI} \qquad \text{etc.,} \qquad (4\text{-}70)$$

and γ_{NaI} is obtained from

$$\gamma_{NaI} = \frac{a_{NaI}}{x_{Na^+} \cdot x_{I^-}} \qquad (4\text{-}71)$$

Flood, Forland, and Grjotheim [2] devised ion-exchange equilibria measurements that, together with activity measurements in the binary systems, were able to give the activity coefficient of components of the mixture.

Calculations based on random distribution of ions can be regarded as only approximate for real mixtures and many modifications have been introduced (e.g., by Blander [14]) to allow for nonrandom mixing.

4-12 THE APPLICATION OF ACTIVITY AND OTHER THERMODYNAMIC MEASUREMENTS TO INVESTIGATION OF STRUCTURE OF MOLTEN SALT SYSTEMS

The methods described above have been applied to the investigation of many molten salt systems, which fall into two broad classes.

Binary Systems That Are Approximately Ideal

Such systems include $CdCl_2 + AgCl$, for which the activity isotherm for $CdCl_2$ at 1003°K is shown in Fig. 4-11; $PbCl_2 + LiCl$; $AgCl + PbCl_2$; $AgCl + LiCl$; $PbCl_2 + CdCl_2$; and many others. For such systems activity coefficients of both components are commonly between 0.90 and 1.00 over the whole range of composition and the heat of mixing is small (often endothermic).

Binary Systems That Are Nonideal

For many systems, e.g., $CdCl_2$ + KCl (Fig. 4-20), activity coefficients are very low, e.g., <0.20 over a considerable part of the composition range. Such systems include also $PbCl_2$ + KCl, $PbCl_2$ + RbCl, $PbCl_2$ + CsCl, $CdCl_2$ + RbCl, $CdCl_2$ + CsCl, NaF + ZrF_4, KF + ZrF_4, and many others. The lowering of activity coefficient in such systems over a range of composition has usually been attributed to removal of the simple components of the mixture in the form of complex ions. For example,

$$CdCl_2 + KCl = KCdCl_3$$
$$CdCl_2 + 2KCl = K_2CdCl_4$$

and

$$CdCl_2 + 4KCl = K_4CdCl_6$$

which lead to the complex ions $CdCl_3^-$, $CdCl_4^{2-}$, and $CdCl_6^{4-}$, respectively. The low values of γ_{CdCl_2} (and γ_{KCl}) at high mole fractions KCl tend to favor the complex ions $CdCl_4^{2-}$ and $CdCl_6^{4-}$ rather than $CdCl_3^-$.

A method to determine the formulas for complex ions in the $CdCl_2$ + KCl and $CdBr_2$ + KBr systems from activity data has been devised by

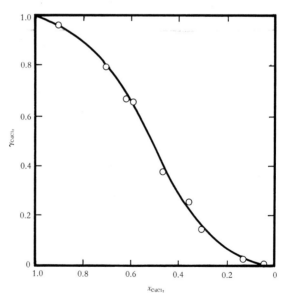

Fig. 4-20. *Activity coefficient of $CdCl_2$ at 900°C in the molten $CdCl_2$ + KCl system. (Adapted from J. L. Barton and H. Bloom, Trans. Faraday Soc., 55, 1792 (1959).)*

Bredig,[15] who used the Temkin method of calculating activities of CdX_2 and KX in these systems. To investigate the formation of complex ions CdX_3^-, CdX_4^{2-}, and CdX_6^{4-}, that is, $CdX_z^{(z-2)^-}$ where $z = 3$, 4, or 6, Bredig deduced the general relation for activities of CdX_2 and KX in the mixture on the assumption that a particular complex ion $CdX_z^{(z-2)^-}$ is formed quantitatively. The following relations then follow from (4-25).

$$a_{CdX_2} = x_{Cd^{2+}} \cdot (x_{X^-})^2$$

$$= \frac{(z-2) - (z-1)x_1}{(z-2) - x_1} \cdot \left(\frac{(2z-4) - (2z-2)x_1}{(2z-4) - (2z-3)x_1}\right)^2 \quad (4\text{-}72)$$

and

$$a_{KX} = x_{K^+} \cdot x_{X^-}$$

$$= \frac{1 - (z-1)(1-x_1)}{1 - (z-2)(1-x_1)} \quad (4\text{-}73)$$

where x_1 is the mole fraction of KX in the mixture; $x_{Cd^{2+}}$, x_{K^+}, and x_{X^-} are the ion fractions of Cd^{2+}, K^+, and X^-, respectively (x_1 values are restricted to those that give activities between 0 and 1).

The activities for the $CdBr_2$ + KBr system calculated by means of (4-72) and (4-73) are shown in Fig. 4-21, together with the experimental

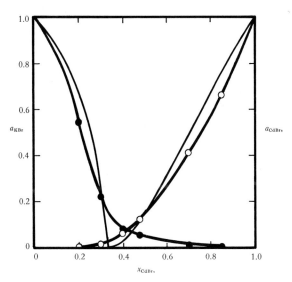

Fig. 4-21. *Activities of $CdBr_2$ and KBr at 600°C in the $CdBr_2$ + KBr system. O, a_{CdBr_2} (experimental); ●, a_{KBr} (experimental); lighter line, theoretical calculation for $CdBr_4^{2-}$ (Bredig [15]).*

data of Lantratov *et al.*[16] for a_{CdBr_2} from emf measurements and the corresponding values of a_{KBr} by Gibbs-Duhem integration (Section 4-5). It can be seen that for the $CdBr_4^{2-}$ complex ion, the experimental activities deviate in the same sense (i.e., both positively or both negatively) from the activities calculated on the bases of (4-72) and (4-73), with $z = 4$. If z is fixed at 3, the experimental a_{CdBr_2} is far above the calculated values. Bredig concludes that $CdBr_4^{2-}$ is the most likely complex ion in the $CdBr_2 + KBr$ system.

For the $CdCl_2 + KCl$ system the same method gives good agreement between calculated and experimental values for the formation of $CdCl_4^{2-}$ at 500°C in the range 0.3–0.7 mole fraction $CdCl_2$. The Bredig method does not give perfect agreement over the whole composition range and at all temperatures for any particular complex ion. It must be regarded as an approximate method that does not allow for the possibility that several complex equilibrium reactions may be taking place simultaneously and that the formation of complex ions from the simple species need not be quantitative.

Van Artsdalen[17] has utilized cryoscopic measurements to calculate equilibrium constants for various complex equilibria in systems, including $CdCl_2 + MCl$ (where $M = Li, Na, K, Cs$), so as to account for the fact that in sodium nitrate solvent the freezing point depression depends on added alkali chloride as well as $CdCl_2$. The equilibrium

$$CdCl_2 + (z - 2)Cl^- = CdCl_z^{(z-2)-}$$

was assumed to account for the effect of the alkali chloride on freezing point depression by $CdCl_2$, and the reaction

$$Cd^{2+} + 4Cl^- = CdCl_4^{2-}$$

with equilibrium constant values of about 1400 at approximately 307°C gave the best agreement with experiment.

Information regarding complex ion equilibria obtained from freezing point depression data is not necessarily applicable at any but low solute concentrations and may not apply in widely different temperature ranges. For the $CdCl_2 + KCl$ system, Lantratov *et al.*[16] have proposed equilibria involving $CdCl_3^-$ and $CdCl_6^{4-}$ from activity measurements. $CdCl_6^{4-}$ will most likely occur at high mole fractions of KCl.

Thermochemical measurements are also very useful in establishing the formulas of complex ions. The results of Kleppa and McCarty[10] for the $MgCl_2 + MCl$ systems (Fig. 4-17) show that in each system there is a maximum in the heat evolved on mixing in the vicinity of 0.6 mole fraction MCl. The complex ion of formula $MgCl_4^{2-}$ would thus be predicted as at $MgCl_2 \cdot$ 2MCl, the composition of the system is 0.67 mole fraction MCl, and the equilibrium reaction

$$MgCl_2 + 2Cl^- = MgCl_4^{2-}$$

would be expected to proceed to its optimum. The formation of this complex can be regarded as very likely to proceed to a large extent in the $MgCl_2 + CsCl$ system, where the maximum in the heat evolved on mixing the reactants reaches the quite high value of 5.5 kcal mole^{-1} at about 0.6 mole fraction CsCl. The graphs of Kleppa's structure parameter $\Delta H_{mix}/x(1-x)$ in fact go through sharply defined minima at precisely 0.67 mole fraction MCl (see Fig. 4-22), confirming that the only complex formed in these systems is $MgCl_4^{2-}$.

The effect of varying the alkali cation is clearly illustrated in Figs. 4-17

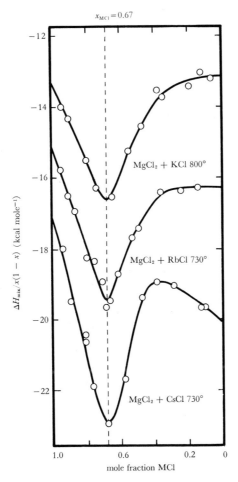

Fig. 4-22. *Isotherms of* $\Delta H_{mix}/x(1-x)$ *for* $MgCl_2 + MCl$ *systems* $(M = K,$ *Rb, Cs)* *(from Kleppa and McCarty* [10]*).*

and 4-22, where the heat evolved on mixing decreases as size of alkali cation decreases corresponding to a decrease in the proportion of complex ion formed. The heat of mixing is quite small in the presence of the small highly polarizing Li^+ (polarizing power = charge/radius^2), this being sufficiently polarizing to distort complexes that would be formed and to render them unstable (see Table 4-4).

It is noteworthy that the ratios of heats of mixing at the maxima in the ΔH_{mix} isotherms are in reasonably close agreement with the inverse ratios of polarizing power of the alkali cations. Thus in the $MgCl_2 + CsCl$ system, the association constant to form $MgCl_4^{2-}$ is high but as Rb^+, K^+, and so on successively replace Cs^+, this association constant diminishes approximately proportionally to the polarizing power of the alkali cation. For $MgCl_2 + LiCl$, simple ions will predominate.

Similar considerations apply to the $PbCl_2 + MCl$ and $CdCl_2 + MCl$ systems. In the former, the maximum heat of mixing is approximately 1.2 kcal mole^{-1} exothermic for $PbCl_2 + KCl$ and in the second it is nearly 3 kcal mole^{-1} exothermic for $CdCl_2 + KCl$. The flattened shapes of the ΔH_{mix} isotherms tend to indicate, particularly in the cadmium systems, that the equilibria involve several different complex ions—possibly $CdCl_3^-$, $CdCl_4^{2-}$, and $CdCl_6^{4-}$ in equilibrium with the simple ions.

4-13 SURFACE TENSION

For molten salts there are many methods of measurement of surface tension based on those used for room temperature liquids. Detachment methods have wide application, although a maximum bubble pressure method appears to be the most suitable and allows precision of ± 0.2 dyne cm^{-1}.

In the bubble pressure method, bubbles are formed by an inert gas, e.g., Ar, using a capillary of platinum or a platinum alloy. The capillary tip must be flat and the apparatus frequently calibrated to prevent errors due to corrosion of the tip. Room temperature calibrating liquids, e.g., water or

Table 4-4 *Polarizing Strength*
(= *charge/radius*^{2}) *of Alkali Cations* (*Relative to* Na^+)

Li^+	1.7	Rb^+	0.5
Na^+	1.0	Cs^+	0.4
K^+	0.6		

benzene, are used. Surface tension σ is calculated by Schroedinger's equation

$$\sigma = \frac{\bar{P}r}{2}\left(1 - \frac{2}{3}\frac{r}{h} - \frac{1}{6}\left(\frac{r}{h}\right)^2 \cdots\right) \tag{4-74}$$

(neglecting higher-order terms); $\bar{P}$ is the maximum bubble pressure, r the radius of capillary, and $h = \bar{P}g/(d - d_1)$ where d is density of the liquid, d_1 the density of the vapor at the same temperature, and g the acceleration due to gravity. Allowance is necessary for depth of immersion of the capillary tip.

For molten salts, surface tension decreases linearly with increase of temperature, i.e., $\sigma = a - bt$, and is related to other thermodynamic quantities. As surface tension is defined as the surface free energy per unit area, we can write

$$\sigma = \frac{G^s}{a} \tag{4-75}$$

where a is the area of the surface and G^s is the surface free energy. The surface entropy per unit area S^s/a is related to temperature coefficient of surface tension by the equation

$$\frac{S^s}{a} = -\frac{d\sigma}{dT} \tag{4-76}$$

and the surface heat content per unit area H^s/a (often called *total surface energy*) is given by

$$\frac{H^s}{a} = \sigma - T\left(\frac{d\sigma}{dT}\right) \tag{4-77}$$

Total surface energy is a constant for each molten salt as the temperature coefficient of surface tension is constant over wide temperature intervals. Surface tension equations and values of total surface energy are given in Table 4-5.

Surface tensions for molten salts are usually higher than for room temperature liquids, but their values are much below those for molten metals. The value of H^s/a appears to be related to degree of ionic character, as values are high for molten salts—usually 150–200 erg cm^{-2}, but for nonpolar liquids the range is between 40 and 65 erg cm^{-2} (e.g., 42.9 for methanol, 59.2 for benzene). Within the molten salts H^s/a has highest values for highly ionic salts but $MgCl_2$, which is not fully dissociated in the melt into ions, has a value of only 76.7 erg cm^{-2}, that is, quite close to the range for covalent liquids.

For binary salt systems, the surface tension isotherms invariably exhibit negative deviation from linearity when plotted against molar composition,

Table 4-5   *Surface Tensions of Pure Molten Salts*

Salt	Surface tension σ at $t°C$ (dyne cm^{-1}) $\left(= erg\ cm^{-2} \right)$	H^s/a (erg cm^{-2})
NaCl	$190.8 - 0.093t$	216.2
NaBr	$145.1 - 0.061t$	161.8
NaI	$147.4 - 0.090t$	171.9
KCl	$155.2 - 0.073t$	175.1
KBr	$142.2 - 0.072t$	161.9
KI	$138.7 - 0.087t$	162.5
NaNO$_3$	$128.3 - 0.039t$	138.9
KNO$_3$	$131.0 - 0.064t$	148.5
PbCl$_2$	$192.1 - 0.110t$	222.1

and these deviations were correlated by Boardman, Palmer, and Heymann [18] with a relation deduced by Guggenheim, namely, for a mixture of liquids 1 and 2 with surface tensions σ_1 and σ_2, respectively,

$$\exp\left(-\frac{\sigma a'}{kT} \right) = x_1 \exp\left(-\frac{\sigma_1 a'}{kT} \right) + x_2 \exp\left(-\frac{\sigma_2 a'}{kT} \right) \qquad (4\text{-}78)$$

where a' is the average area per molecule in the surface plane and σ is the surface tension of the liquid mixture of composition x_1 mole fraction 1 and x_2 mole fraction 2.   For an equimolar mixture, this becomes

$$\sigma = \bar{\sigma} - \left(\frac{\Delta^2 a'}{8kT} \right) \qquad (4\text{-}79)$$

where $\bar{\sigma}$ is the mean of σ_1 and σ_2 and Δ is the difference between σ_1 and σ_2.

For the CdCl$_2$ + PbCl$_2$ system the experimental value of σ is greater than that calculated from (4-79), and this deviation is in the same direction as conductance (see Section 5-2), but for most binary molten salt systems the measured surface tension for the equimolar mixture is less than that calculated from (4-79).   The results for systems CdCl$_2$ + PbCl$_2$, AgCl + PbCl$_2$, and PbCl$_2$ + KCl are shown in Fig. 4-23.   It is difficult to make structural deductions from surface tension isotherms.   The AgCl + PbCl$_2$ system is reasonably close to ideal as shown by activity determinations, but PbCl$_2$ + KCl is far from ideal, yet the surface tension isotherms for both systems deviate from the ideal values to much the same extent.

Bloom, Davis, and James [19] used the values of surface heat of mixing as an additive quantity to define an ideal solution.   The use of this quantity is particularly suitable for molten salts, as H^s/a is constant over a wide range of

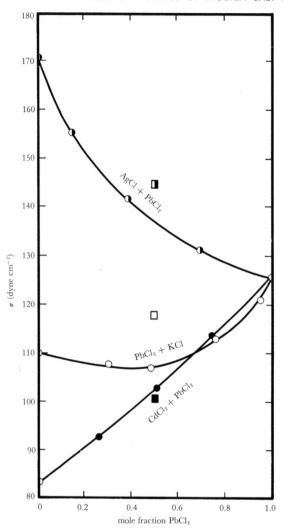

Fig. 4-23. *Surface tension isotherms at 600°C for molten salt systems. The three squares represent values calculated by Eq. (4-79) for the equimolar mixtures. (Adapted from Boardman et al.[18])*

temperatures.   Hence the value of H^s/a for the ideal mixture of two molten salts should be given by

$$\frac{H^s}{a} = x_1 \left(\frac{H^s}{a}\right)_1 + x_2 \left(\frac{H^s}{a}\right)_2 \qquad (4\text{-}80)$$

and the excess surface energy (or heat) of mixing would be zero; that is,

$$\left(\frac{\Delta H^s}{a}\right)_{\text{mix}} = \frac{H^s}{a} - \left[x_1 \left(\frac{H^s}{a}\right)_1 + x_2 \left(\frac{H^s}{a}\right)_2\right] = 0 \qquad (4\text{-}81)$$

for an ideal system.

Many molten salt systems that are known to be ideal do in fact have zero values of excess surface energies, but some, such as $PbCl_2 + RbCl$ (investigated by Dahl and Duke [20]), have negative excess surface energies, and in this system $-(\Delta H^s/a)_{\text{mix}}$ has a maximum at 0.5 mole fraction composition. This exothermic surface reaction has been correlated with the formation of complex ions and $PbCl_3^-$ would appear to be the most logical formula from this evidence.

Other derived quantities have been investigated for their structural significance, e.g., the parachor $[P]$ (Sugden), which is given by

$$[P] = \left(\frac{M}{d_{\text{liq}} - d_{\text{vap}}}\right) \sigma^{1/4} \qquad (4\text{-}82)$$

but its use is not helpful for molten salts, as $[P]$ is strongly temperature dependent.   Even the form proposed by Batchinski [21]

$$[P] = \left(\frac{M}{d_{\text{liq}} - d_{\text{sol}}}\right) \sigma^{1/4} \qquad (4\text{-}83)$$

is considerably temperature dependent, and the additivity relations associated with the parachor have not been investigated for molten salts.

The values of surface tension are important in calculating parameters associated with various structural theories of molten salts.   For example, in developing an equation of state for molten salts, Bockris and Richards [11] used surface tension measurements to calculate the energy E_h to form holes in molten salts from the equation

$$E_h = 4\pi r_h^2 \sigma \qquad (4\text{-}84)$$

where r_h is the radius of the mean hole.

Stillinger [22] has calculated surface tensions for molten salts from a statistical mechanical theory developed by Reiss et al. for the amount of reversible work necessary to introduce a spherical cavity of a definite radius into the liquid composed of ions.   Results of these calculations correlate quite well with experiment for molten alkali halides, and this can be taken as additional evidence to demonstrate the essentially ionic structure of these molten salts.

REFERENCES

1. Temkin, M., *Acta Physicochim. URSS*, **20**, 411 (1945).
2. Flood, H., Forland, T., and Grjotheim, K., in *The Physical Chemistry of Melts*, p. 46, Institution of Mining and Metallurgy, London, 1953; Forland, T., in *Fused Salts* (B. R. Sundheim, ed.), p. 63, McGraw-Hill, New York, 1964.
3. Hildebrand, J. H., and Salstrom, E. J., *J. Am. Chem. Soc.*, **52**, 4641 (1930); **54**, 4257 (1932).
4. Barton, J. L., and Bloom, H., *J. Phys. Chem.*, **60**, 1413 (1956); *Trans. Faraday Soc.*, **55**, 1792 (1959).
5. Rosner, G. A., and Jellinek, K., *Z. Phys. Chem. (Leipzig)*, **A143**, 51 (1929).
6. Kordes, E., Bergmann, W., and Vogel, W., *Z. Elektrochem.*, **55**, 600 (1951).
7. Kleppa, O. J., *J. Phys. Chem.*, **64**, 1937 (1960).
8. Bloom, H., and Tricklebank, S. B., *Aust. J. Chem.*, **19**, 187 (1966).
9. Davis, H. T., and Rice, S. A., *J. Chem. Phys.*, **41**, 14 (1964).
10. Kleppa, O. J., and McCarty, F. G., *J. Phys. Chem.*, **70**, 1249 (1966).
11. Bockris, J. O'M., and Richards, N. E., *Proc. Roy. Soc.*, **A241**, 44 (1957).
12. Bloom, H., Boyd, P. W. D., Laver, J. L., and Wong, J., *Aust. J. Chem.*, **19**, 1591 (1966).
13. Boardman, N. K., Dorman, F. H., and Heymann, E., *J. Phys. Chem.*, **53**, 375 (1949).
14. Blander, M., in *Molten Salt Chemistry* (M. Blander, ed.), p. 127, Interscience, New York, 1964.
15. Bredig, M. A., *J. Chem. Phys.*, **37**, 451 (1962).
16. Lantratov, M. F., and Shevlyakova, T. N., *J. Appl. Chem. USSR* (English trans.), **34**, 1017 (1961); Lantratov, M. F., and Alabyshev, A. F., *J. Appl. Chem. USSR* (English trans.), **26**, 253, 321 (1953); **27**, 685 (1954).
17. Van Artsdalen, E. R., *J. Phys. Chem.*, **60**, 172 (1956).
18. Boardman, N. K., Palmer, A. R., and Heymann, E., *Trans. Faraday Soc.*, **51**, 277 (1955).
19. Bloom, H., Davis, F. G., and James, D. W., *Trans. Faraday Soc.*, **56**, 1179 (1960).
20. Dahl, J. L., and Duke, F. R., *J. Phys. Chem.*, **62**, 1142, 1498 (1958).
21. Batchinski, A. I., Quoted by E. A. Ukshe, *Russian Chem. Rev.* (English trans.), **34**, 146 (1965), Ref. 165.
22. Stillinger, F. H., in *Molten Salt Chemistry* (M. Blander, ed.), p. 1, Interscience, New York, 1964.

5

Transport Properties of
Molten Salts

The study of transport properties of molten salts has received impetus from at least two directions. Properties such as electrical conductance, viscosity, and transference number have been used to arrive at structural information on molten salts; also, together with thermal conductivity and other properties, such properties are of considerable practical importance in metallurgical and electrowinning industries.

As for any other kinetic studies, unique structural information cannot be obtained from transport properties, and combination with other methods is necessary in order to arrive at convincing structural models.

5-1 THE ELECTROLYSIS OF MOLTEN SALTS— APPLICATION OF FARADAY'S LAWS

Michael Faraday studied about fifty molten salts in order to test the validity of the laws that bear his name. In actual fact it is difficult to demonstrate the validity of Faraday's laws for molten salts because of evaporation or

76

distillation of the metal separated in the molten state and because of dissolution or secondary reaction of the diffused anode product with the molten salt. Loss of current efficiency usually results; this depends on the salt temperature and current density, as well as materials forming the electrodes, and so on. Commonly observed current efficiencies in industrial electrolytic processes are given in Table 5-1.

The current efficiency depends strongly on temperature; for example, in the electrolysis of $PbCl_2$, current efficiency for a particular electrode arrangement may vary from 96.3% at 540°C (40° above the melting point) to 38.0% at 900°C and zero at the boiling point (956°C).

To increase current efficiency, diffusion from the electrodes of products that cause secondary reaction to produce the starting material must be kept to a minimum; hence, electrodes must be as far apart as possible and temperature as low as possible. Current density should be as high as possible, although this is limited by the onset of the "anode effect" (see Chapter 9). Experiments with molten lead chloride have shown that at the optimum current density and temperature, and with both electrodes separated by diaphragms to prevent mixing of electrolysis products, current efficiencies of 99.98% may be attained. Similar observations apply in other cases. It is therefore concluded that with proper precautions to prevent loss of electrolysis products, Faraday's laws apply perfectly to molten salt electrolysis.

5-2 ELECTRICAL CONDUCTANCE OF MOLTEN SALTS

Accurate determination of conductance of molten salts is difficult, as the specific conductance κ of most molten salt systems is of the order of from 1 to 10 ohm^{-1} cm^{-1}. Since

$$\kappa = \frac{C}{R} \qquad (5-1)$$

Table 5-1 *Cathode Current Efficiency in Industrial Electrolytic Processes Involving Molten Salts*

Element produced	Electrolyte	Current efficiency (%)
Sodium	NaOH	55
Magnesium	$MgCl_2 + NaCl + KCl$	75
Calcium	$CaCl_2$	70
Aluminum	$Al_2O_3 + Na_3AlF_6 + AlF_3 + CaF_2$	90

where C is the cell constant and R ohm the electrical resistance, the measurement of κ with an accuracy of, say, 0.2% with conventional conductance bridges requires cell constants of between 100 and 1000. To achieve high cell constants, cells with capillaries between the electrodes are employed. In Fig. 5-1, a simple type of capillary cell is illustrated. Such cells are constructed of a high melting glass, e.g., vitreous silica, with platinum or molybdenum electrodes. For higher melting or very corrosive salts, alumina or magnesia capillaries have been used advantageously. Cell constant is determined by calibration at 25°C or another convenient temperature with aqueous KCl solution.

Temperature coefficient of conductance is usually about 0.1–0.5% per degree, hence temperature constancy and uniformity are very essential. Measurement of temperature is commonly by means of noble metal, for example, Pt versus Pt + 13% Rh thermocouples, which are calibrated at the melting points of metals and salts.

Considerable discrepancies between measured values of electrical conductance for a particular electrolyte have been reported. Figure 5-2 gives the results of a number of different investigations for molten KCl. The

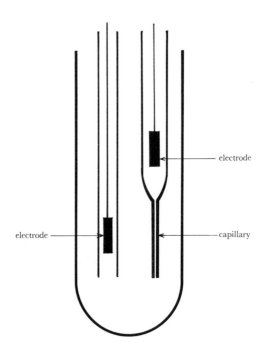

electrode

electrode ——— capillary

Fig. 5-1. *Capillary conductance cell (from Bloom and Heymann* [3]*).*

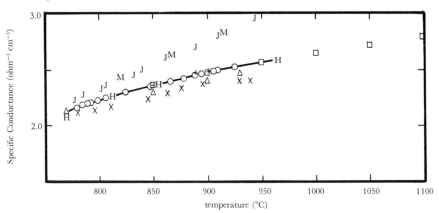

Fig. 5-2. *Specific conductance of pure KCl.* ○, *Van Artsdalen and Yaffe; H, Huber, Potter, and St. Clair;* ✕, *Karpachev, Stromberg, and Padchainova;* △, *Biltz and Klemm;* □, *Edwards, Taylor, Russell, and Maranville;* +, *Lee and Pearson; J, Jaeger and Kampa; M, Mantzell (from Van Artsdalen and Yaffe* [7]).

results of different investigations differ here by up to 20%. Part of the discrepancy may be due to faulty design of the conductance bridge, which to read resistance correctly must allow compensation of both ohmic and capacitative components of the cell impedance over a wide range of frequencies. Platinizing of the electrodes is not helpful for molten salts, because sintering of platinum black produces white or grey platinum on heating; however, electrode polarization is not usually significant. Platinization is usually regarded as necessary when the cell is being calibrated using aqueous KCl solution.

An alternating current Wheatstone bridge is normally used, with the elimination of reactance due to electrode capacitance and lead capacitance, by plotting apparent resistance against some function of frequency (e.g., the square root) and extrapolating to infinite frequency. Direct current ("four-probe") methods have been used successfully. King and Duke [1] measured conductance of the molten alkali metal nitrates in this manner.

Equivalent Conductance

From specific conductance κ, equivalent weight e, and density d, the equivalent conductance Λ, that is, the conductance of one equivalent of electrolyte between parallel planar electrodes 1 cm apart, can be calculated from the equation

$$\Lambda = \frac{\kappa e}{d} = \kappa V_e \tag{5-2}$$

where V_e ml = equivalent volume of the molten salt.

For mixtures of molten salts,

$$\Lambda = \frac{\kappa \bar{e}}{d} \tag{5-3}$$

where $\bar{e}$ = mean equivalent weight calculated from the equation

$$\bar{e} = f_1 e_1 + f_2 e_2 \tag{5-4}$$

where f_1, f_2 = equivalent fractions of components 1, 2 and e_1, e_2 are their equivalent weights.

For example, for x mole fraction of KBr mixed with $(1 - x)$ mole fraction BaBr$_2$,

$$\bar{e} = \frac{x e_1}{x + 2(1 - x)} + \frac{2(1 - x) e_2}{x + 2(1 - x)} \tag{5-5}$$

Temperature Dependence of Conductance

Over a temperature range of no more than, say, 200° (depending on the individual molten salt), κ bears an approximately linear relationship to temperature, as is shown in Fig. 5-2 for KCl. Over a greater temperature range, Kohlrausch's formula

$$\kappa = a + bt + ct^2 \tag{5-6}$$

where t = temperature in degrees centigrade, is often used.

Activation Energy for Conductance

Frenkel applied the Arrhenius equation to explain the change of conductance with absolute temperature. Thus

$$\Lambda = A_\Lambda \exp\left(-\frac{E_\Lambda}{RT}\right) \tag{5-7}$$

where A_Λ is a constant for a particular molten salt and E_Λ is the activation energy for conductance. Eyring's theory of rate processes has been applied to molten electrolytes, giving the equation

$$\Lambda = 5.18 \times 10^{18} z_i (D + 2) l_i^2 \exp\left(\frac{\Delta S^\ddagger}{R}\right) \exp\left(-\frac{\Delta H^\ddagger}{RT}\right) \tag{5-8}$$

where z_i = charge on ion, D = dielectric constant of the molten salt, l_i =

half the migration distance of the conducting ion, and $\Delta S^{\ddagger}$, $\Delta H^{\ddagger}$ are entropy and heat of activation of the conduction process, respectively.

The evaluation of Eq. (5-8) requires certain assumptions, for example, D is not known for molten electrolytes but many investigators arbitrarily assign to it a value of 3 or 4. The most common use for Eq. (5-8) is the calculation of $\Delta S^{\ddagger}$. Fortunately a considerable variation of D is possible without much affecting the value of $\Delta S^{\ddagger}$ thus calculated. (A change from $D = 3$ to $D = 15$ makes all $\Delta S^{\ddagger}$ values approximately 2 eu more negative.)

From the variation of κ with T, the expression

$$\kappa = A \exp\left(\frac{-E_{\kappa}}{RT}\right) \tag{5-9}$$

the activation energy for specific conductance E_{κ} can be readily calculated. It can be shown that

$$E_{\Lambda} = E_{\kappa} + RT^2\alpha \tag{5-10}$$

where R is the gas constant and α is the volume coefficient of expansion. As α is positive, E_{Λ} is necessarily greater than E_{κ}. In order to evaluate E_{Λ}, the values of $\log_{10} \Lambda$ are graphed against $1/T$ and the slope measured. This slope is usually independent of temperature over a considerable temperature range; see, for example, Fig. 5-3 for the molten barium halides. E_{Λ} is

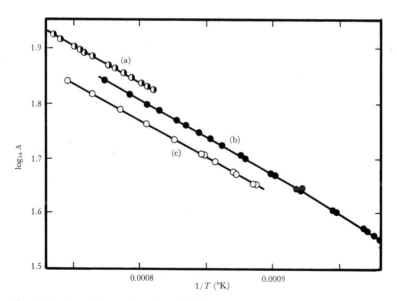

Fig. 5-3. *Log₁₀ Λ plotted against 1/T for the molten barium halides: (a) BaCl₂; (b) BaI₂; (c) BaBr₂ (from Bockris et al.[8]).*

obtained for each salt by multiplying the slope of the line by $-2.303R$, i.e., -4.57 cal mole^{-1}. Provided all but the last term on the right-hand side of Eq. (5-8) are independent of temperature, it is clear that $\Delta H^{\ddagger} = E_\Lambda$. E_κ can be obtained in an analogous way from variation of log κ with $1/T$.

Equations (5-7) and (5-9) should apply separately to conduction by anion and cation, respectively, but Barzakowskii,[2] Bloom and Heymann,[3] and others have shown that it applies over a considerable range of temperature to a variety of molten salts; hence, in the complete equation

$$\Lambda = A_1 \exp\left(\frac{-E_1}{RT}\right) + A_2 \exp\left(\frac{-E_2}{RT}\right) \qquad (5\text{-}11)$$

where E_1 is activation energy for one ion, e.g., the cation, and E_2 the value for the other ion, it follows that either

$$E_1 \simeq E_2 \qquad E_1 \gg E_2 \qquad \text{or} \qquad E_2 \ll E_1$$

For mixtures of molten salts, also, (5-7) and (5-9) are applicable.

The Electrical Conductance of Pure Molten Salts

The wide range of melting points for salts makes it necessary to compare conductance at corresponding temperatures. As with molar volumes, 1.1 T_{fus} will be used.

Biltz and Klemm [4] noted a correlation between conductance of the molten salt and the position of the cationic element in the periodic table and postulated that the conductance increases with the ionic nature of the bond. Salts with a high degree of covalent bonding, for example, mercury halides, are poor conductors, whereas the alkali halides and other ionic salts are very good conductors, hence they are mainly in the form of unassociated ions in the melt. The temperature coefficient of conductance also increases with the covalent nature of the substance.

Table 5-2 presents equivalent conductance values for some molten salts at temperature 1.1 T_{fus}. The decrease of conductance from LiCl to CsCl is typical of the trend for the group I halides.

Group II halides do not in general conduct as well as group I halides. BeCl$_2$ has the very low equivalent conductance of 0.22 ohm^{-1} cm^2 equiv^{-1} at temperature 1.1 T_{fus}. This molten salt also has a high vapor pressure and a short liquid range (about 107°C), thus suggesting a high degree of covalency in agreement with its low electrical conductance. Molten BeCl$_2$ near its melting point probably has a polymeric structure in equilibrium with ionic entities. The conductance of the melt increases very considerably on heating, indicating that the structure breaks up at higher temperatures.

Table 5-2   *Equivalent Conductance* Λ *at 1.1* T_{fus} *for Pure Molten Salts*

Salt	m.p. (°K)	$1.1\,T_{\text{fus}}$	$\Lambda\ (\text{ohm}^{-1}\,\text{cm}^2\,\text{equiv}^{-1})$
LiCl	883	971	178.5
NaCl	1074	1181	152.3
KCl	1043	1147	122.4
RbCl	995	1094	99.8
CsCl	918	1010	86.7
$CdCl_2$	841	925	57.8
$PbCl_2$	773	850	52.3

For molten group II halides, Markov and Delimarskii [5] deduced constitutional changes on heating in terms of the equilibria

$$MX_2 \rightleftharpoons MX^+ + X^- \rightleftharpoons M^{2+} + 2X^- \qquad (5\text{-}12)$$

Derivation of the equilibrium constants from conductance measurements alone is not possible.

For transition and posttransition metal halides, various complex species are generally assumed to be present in addition to the simple ions M^{2+} and X^-. For molten zinc chloride, Mackenzie and Murphy [6] found that the Arrhenius equation (5-9) was not obeyed, that is, the relation between $\log \kappa$ and $1/T$ was not linear. This is illustrated in Fig. 5-4. The conducting entities close to the freezing point when the salt is a very poor conductor of electricity are thought to be in equilibrium with a largely molecular structure, and the proportion of ions in the melt is assumed to increase rapidly with increase of temperature; that is, conductance increases rapidly. These structural changes are illustrated in Fig. 2-8. As temperature increases, equilibria involving the polymeric network structure and simpler ions, including Zn^{2+}, $ZnCl^+$, $ZnCl_3^-$, and $ZnCl_4^{2-}$ are thought to occur.

Mercury (II) halides have low viscosities in the molten state (unlike $ZnCl_2$), hence their high vapor pressures and short liquid range indicate that although they are not polymerized, they have, in accordance with their low equivalent conductances, molecular species as the main entities in equilibrium with the ions HgX^+, HgX_3^-, and X^-.

Heat of Activation for Conductance of Pure Molten Salts

From Eq. (5-8) the values of $\Delta H^\ddagger$ and $\Delta S^\ddagger$ can be determined, provided the variation of Λ with change of temperature is known. Table 5-3 gives values of $\Delta H^\ddagger$, $-\Delta S^\ddagger$, and E_κ for some molten group I chlorides.

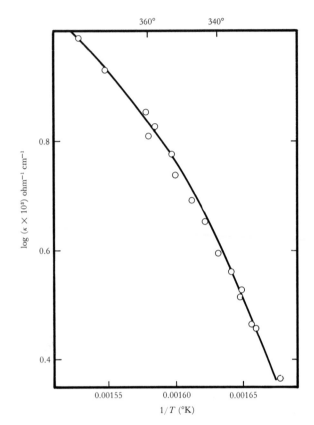

Fig. 5-4 *Relation between log κ and 1/T for molten ZnCl₂ (from Mackenzie and Murphy [6]).*

From Li to Cs, i.e., with increasing cation size, there is in general, an increase of $\Delta H^{\ddagger}$ for each of the different halides. In contradiction of Eq. (5-7), there is in practice a slight temperature variation of $\Delta H^{\ddagger}$ and the direction of this variation is dependent on the salt; for example, for NaI the value of $\Delta H^{\ddagger}$ is almost constant at 3.2 kcal mole⁻¹ from 660° to 914°C, while for NaCl the change is from 2.8 kcal mole⁻¹ at 820°C to 3.2 kcal mole⁻¹ at 1020°C. For CsI the direction is reversed and at 630°C is 6.4 kcal mole⁻¹ changing to 4.9 kcal mole⁻¹ at 880°C.

Yaffe and Van Artsdalen [7] considered the heat of activation to be dependent on at least two opposing factors. As the melt expands with rising temperature, the total coulombic forces among the constituent ions tend to lessen and thus heat of activation for migration should decrease. On the other hand, any particular ion has fewer nearest neighbors on increase of

Table 5-3   *Values of $\Delta H^{\ddagger}$, $-\Delta S^{\ddagger}$, and E_{κ} for Some Molten Group I Chlorides*

Salt	$\Delta H^{\ddagger}$ (or E_{Λ}) (kcal mole^{-1})	$-\Delta S^{\ddagger}$ (eu mole^{-1})	E_{κ} at 850°C (kcal mole^{-1})
LiCl	2.1	6	1.47
NaCl	2.9	6	1.98
KCl	3.4	7	2.29
RbCl	4.3	6	3.44
CsCl	4.9	6	4.29

temperature due to an increase in the number of holes in the lattice. Hence the attractive force per nearest neighbor will increase and so there will be an increase of the heat of activation. The second effect will predominate where there is a greater disparity between ion size, while the first will predominate when ions tend toward the same size. Hence, for salts of Li and Na, $\Delta H^{\ddagger}$ tends to increase with increasing temperature but the reverse is true for salts of Rb and Cs. This generalization can be taken as being a working rule only and there are several exceptions, for example, the temperature-independent value of $\Delta H^{\ddagger}$ for NaI.

For the group II chlorides the values of $\Delta H^{\ddagger}$ are somewhat higher than for those of group I, but are generally less dependent on temperature, with some exceptions (e.g., for SrBr$_2$ $\Delta H^{\ddagger}$ is 13.9 kcal mole^{-1} at its melting point (657°C), falling rapidly to 6.9 at 693°C and thereafter changing very little with increase of temperature).

For beryllium chloride $\Delta H^{\ddagger}$ changes from 235 to 25 kcal mole^{-1} over a 45°C range of temperature, as shown in Fig. 5-5. This is consistent with the dissociation model already proposed for BeCl$_2$, for which conduction at lower temperatures involves the energy required to break bonds, hence to split off conducting units from the polymerized structure, in addition to the activation energy for migration. At temperatures well above the melting point the structure is sufficiently degraded by thermal dissociation to give a large proportion of ions free to conduct. The value of $\Delta H^{\ddagger}$ is thus diminished by the energy of bond breaking to that for hole making and the jumping of ions. As the energies for hole making and jumping are very small compared with that of bond breaking at temperatures near the melting point, the difference in $\Delta H^{\ddagger}$ from the melting point to the higher temperature is about 200 kcal mole^{-1}, which is approximately the same as the energy required to remove a molecule of BeCl$_2$ from the polymeric species. At higher temperatures Bockris et al.[8] consider that molten BeCl$_2$ is present as BeCl^{+} and Cl^{-}.

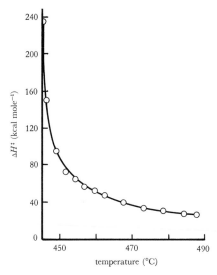

Fig. 5-5. *Energy of activation for conduction for molten BeCl₂. (From the results of Yu. K. Delimarskii, I. N. Sheiko, and V. G. Feshchenko, Zh. Fiz. Khim.,* **29,** *1499 (1955).)*

Entropy of Activation for Molten Salts

From Table 5-3 it can be seen that the entropy of activation for conductance is approximately -6 eu for molten alkali chlorides. For the other molten alkali halides the value of $\Delta S^{\ddagger}$ does not depart greatly from -6 eu, the greatest variation being shown by molten LiI with a $\Delta S^{\ddagger}$ value of -8 eu. Considering the gross assumptions made for the extraction of $\Delta S^{\ddagger}$, little significance can be placed on such small differences and the value of $\Delta S^{\ddagger}$ may be taken as -6 eu for all molten alkali halides.

Most molten group IIA halides also have $\Delta S^{\ddagger}$ values close to -6 eu but halides of beryllium, zinc, and mercury have much different values. Close to the melting point $\Delta S^{\ddagger}$ for molten $ZnCl_2$ is over $+70$ eu, falling at first rapidly, then less so, to -3 eu over a temperature increase of 350°. Similar but less dramatic changes are observed for the other zinc halides. For molten $BeCl_2$, $\Delta S^{\ddagger}$ changes from about $+300$ eu at 445°C to approximately $+12$ eu at 490°C. Although the quantitative significance of $\Delta S^{\ddagger}$ is not well understood for molten salts, there is a striking difference between the approximately constant values of -6 eu for the largely unassociated salts on the one hand, and the positive and more variable values for the largely associated molten salts on the other hand.

The Electrical Conductance of Binary Molten Salt Systems

From the experimental values of specific conductance and density, the equivalent conductances of molten salt mixtures can be calculated by means of Eqs. (5-3) and (5-4). The use of equivalent rather than specific or molar conductance is particularly important in consideration of deviations from ideal mixing in molten salt systems, as the same number of unit electric charges (on ions assumed initially to be unassociated) will always be under consideration. Hence, equivalent conductance isotherms are the most useful when deducing structural information from conductance measurements. Deviations from ideal conductance isotherms are explained in terms of ionic interaction, sometimes with the formation of complex species.

Equivalent conductance (and equivalent volume) isotherms should strictly be plotted as a function of equivalent fraction of one component. It is customary, however, to plot equivalent conductance against mole fraction or mole percent composition, as is done for molar volume. There is, of course, no difference for binary systems involving like ions (i.e., anions or cations) with the same number of charges, but when one like ion does not have the same charge as the other (e.g., in the $AgCl + PbCl_2$ system), the plotting of Λ versus mole fraction will lead to isotherms that do not have the same shape as Λ graphed against equivalent fraction.

The ideal conductance isotherm is taken to be linear with respect to molar composition; that is, the partial conductances of each of the constituents of the mixture are additive. Thus for a mixture of x_1, x_2 mole fractions of components 1 and 2 having equivalent conductances Λ_1 and Λ_2, respectively, at a particular temperature, the conductance of the mixture based on the additivity of conductance is given by

$$\Lambda = x_1\Lambda_1 + x_2\Lambda_2 \qquad (5\text{-}13)$$

If the solution is ideal (for conductance), the measured value of Λ will be the same as calculated by (5-13). There will, however, usually be a difference between the measured Λ and that calculated. This difference can be represented by the excess conductance of mixing $\Delta\Lambda^E$. (By analogy with ΔG^E, etc., $\Delta\Lambda^E$ could be abbreviated to Λ^E.) If $\Delta\Lambda^E$ is zero, the molten salt system is ideal. Very few systems have in fact been found to have zero values of $\Delta\Lambda^E$. The majority have negative deviations from additivity of conductance, while a few systems have positive $\Delta\Lambda^E$ values.

There is a correlation between equivalent conductance and molar volume isotherms, although the deviations are always in opposite directions. Thus an ideal system also has a linear plot of molar volume against mole fraction, that is, ΔV^E (or abbreviated to V^E) is zero. This pattern may be

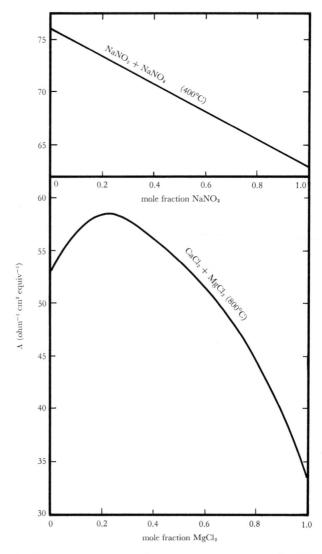

Fig. 5-6. *Equivalent conductance* Λ *of molten salt systems.* $(NaNO_2 + NaNO_3$ *system from H. Bloom, I. W., Knaggs, J. J. Molloy, and D. Welch, Trans. Faraday Soc.,* **49,** *1458 (1953); $CaCl_2 + MgCl_2$ system from the results of R. W. Huber, E. V. Potter, and H. W. St. Clair, U.S. Bur. Mines Rept. Invest.* **4858** *(1952).)*

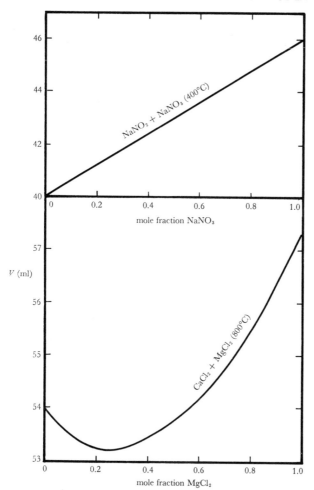

Fig. 5-7. *Molar volumes of molten salt systems. ($NaNO_2 + NaNO_3$ system from H. Bloom, I. W. Knaggs, J. J. Molloy, and D. Welch, Trans. Faraday Soc., **49,** 1458 (1953); $CaCl_2 + MgCl_2$ system from the results of R. W. Huber, E. V. Potter, and H. W. St. Clair, U.S. Bur. Mines Rept. Invest. **4858** (1952).)*

compared with the thermodynamic properties, for example, for ideal systems activity coefficients are equal to unity and ΔH_{mix} is zero.

The molten salt system $NaNO_2 + NaNO_3$ is ideal, as shown in Fig. 5-6 for equivalent conductance and Fig. 5-7 for molar volume at 400°C. In this system the chemical compositions and structures of the components are very similar and the difference between conductances of the individual salts is very small (13 ohm^{-1} cm^2 equiv^{-1} at $400°C$). For this system, $\Delta\Lambda^E$ is thus zero.

The heat of activation for conductance is also approximately the same for molten $NaNO_2$ and $NaNO_3$ (3 kcal mole^{-1}) and is practically constant over the whole of the mixture composition range. Thus the substitution of NO_3^- for NO_2^- has little effect on the conductance properties of the system.

Nonideal Binary Salt Systems

Systems that have negative $\Delta\Lambda^E$ may be subdivided according to the extent of the negative deviations from the additivity of conductance. A large group of systems, including $AgCl + AgBr$ and $PbCl_2 + PbBr_2$, have linear molar volume isotherms ($\Delta V^E = 0$) but relatively small negative deviations from ideal additivity of conductance ($\Delta\Lambda^E < 0$). These systems are not strictly ideal in thermodynamic properties; hence, additivity of molar volumes is not a very rigorous test of ideal mixing. For systems for which $\Delta V^E = 0$, however, the relatively small departures of conductance, etc., from the ideal make it clear that mainly physical forces of interaction are involved on mixing. For such systems it can be noted that (1) like ions have the same number of charges, and (2) the difference between equivalent conductances of the components is small.

Table 5-4 compares a number of systems for which $\Delta V^E = 0$ and which have relatively small negative values of $\Delta\Lambda^E$. The effects of different radii of the replacing ions in the binary systems and difference between equivalent conductances of the pure component salts (at arbitrary temperatures) on the percent of deviation from additivity of conductance of the equimolar mixtures are shown.

Table 5-4

System	Radii of replacing ions ($\mathring{A}$)	Difference between Λ of components	Deviation from additivity of equivalent conductance in the equimolar mixture (%)
$AgCl + AgBr$	Cl$^-$, 1.81; Br$^-$, 1.95	15	1.5
$PbCl_2 + PbBr_2$	Cl$^-$, 1.81; Br$^-$, 1.95	9	2
$CdCl_2 + CdBr_2$	Cl$^-$, 1.81; Br$^-$, 1.95	15	2.5
$NaCl + KCl$	Na$^+$, 0.95; K$^+$, 1.33	24	8
$AgCl + PbCl_2$	Ag$^+$, 1.26; Pb^{2+}, 1.21	73	20
$LiCl + KCl$	Li$^+$, 0.60; K$^+$, 1.33	85	26

Deviations from linear conductance isotherms are thus related semi-quantitatively to differences between conductances of the component salts and to differences in radii of the replacing ions (except for Ag^+, Pb^{2+}). For the $AgCl + PbCl_2$ system the replacement of a singly charged ion by a doubly charged ion appears to be responsible for the large deviation from additivity. (If, however, Λ is plotted against equivalent fraction, the percent of deviation of Λ from additivity in the equimolar mixture is only about 7% and is practically zero from about 0.66 mole fraction $AgCl$ to pure $AgCl$.) For the $LiCl + KCl$ system deviations from additive conductance lead to a shallow minimum at about 0.8 mole fraction KCl, but in other systems in this class conductance minima are not found. Various physical explanations have been advanced for the relatively small deviations from ideal conductance of the systems in Table 5-4, but there has been no theory advanced capable of adequately explaining the shape of the conductance isotherms in quantitative terms. In all systems in this class the heat of activation varies in a more or less regular manner over the composition range.

Systems That Have Large Negative Deviations from Ideal Conductance

Figure 5-8 shows the equivalent conductance isotherms at 720°C for the systems $PbCl_2 + MCl$ (M = Na, K, Rb, Cs). The increasing deviations from additive conductance in the sequence of ions $Na^+ < K^+ < Rb^+ < Cs^+$ replacing Pb^{2+} are evident. (Broken lines represent values extrapolated at temperatures below those of crystallization.)

The system $PbCl_2 + NaCl$ is close to ideal ($\Delta\Lambda^E$ is small when Λ is plotted against equivalent fraction), but for $PbCl_2 + KCl$, $PbCl_2 + RbCl$, and $PbCl_2 + CsCl$ increasingly deep minima are present. Thus the substitution of the more highly conducting K^+ for $\frac{1}{2}Pb^{2+}$ causes a decrease of conductance instead of the anticipated increase. This phenomenon is common to many binary systems, particularly in cases where the phase diagrams show that intermediate solid compounds are formed. Other examples are $MgCl_2 + KCl$, $AlF_3 + NaF$, $CdCl_2 + KCl$, $CdCl_2 + RbCl$, and $CdCl_2 + CsCl$.

Conductance minima are usually accompanied by maxima in $\Delta H^\ddagger$, hence a maximum of $d\Lambda/dT$, as shown in Fig. 5-9 for the $PbCl_2 + KCl$ system. In this class of molten salt system, the molar volume isotherms show positive deviations from additivity, i.e., $\Delta V^E > 0$. See Fig. 4-19. In such systems the results can be explained by the postulate that complex ions of low mobility are produced by mixing the component salts. Thus in the $PbCl_2 + MCl$ systems the results could be explained by the loss of Cl^- and Pb^{2+} as one or more types of complex ions of stoichiometry $PbCl_3^-$, $PbCl_4^{2-}$, and $PbCl_6^{4-}$ are formed on adding KCl to $PbCl_2$. The complex ions are

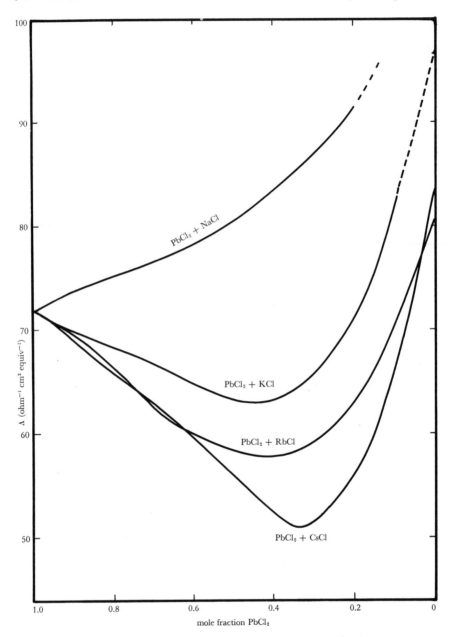

Fig. 5-8. *Equivalent conductance* Λ *of molten salt systems at 720°C (from H. Bloom, Pure Appl. Chem.,* **7**, *389 (1963)).*

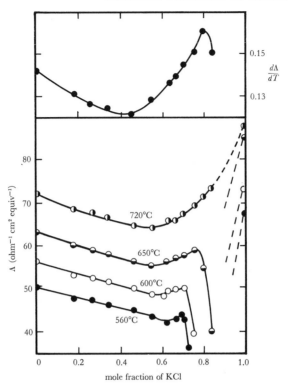

Fig. 5-9. *Equivalent conductance and its temperature coefficient for the $PbCl_2 + KCl$ system (from Bloom and Heymann [3]).*

relatively large and will have low mobilities; hence, $\Delta \Lambda^E < 0$ and conductance minima tend to be formed at compositions related to the maximum concentration of complexes.

The effect of different alkali cation is interesting. The role of the alkali chloride is to provide additional chloride ions to enable Pb^{2+} to expand its coordination shell, but there is obviously a competition between M^+ and Pb^{2+} for Cl^- in the densely populated ionic environment. The result of the competition will depend on the relative attracting power of the alkali ion, Li^+ being the most chloride attracting (i.e., of greatest polarizing power) and Cs^+ the least. The extent to which complex ions are formed in these binary systems will therefore be governed by the radius of the alkali metal ion accompanying the ligand. Thus the addition of $CsCl$ to $PbCl_2$ would favor complex ion formation more than addition of $RbCl$, and so on, and the relative effects on conductance would follow. Complex ion formation would lead to a change of packing in the melt and the formation of larger holes would ensue, thus explaining the positive values of ΔV^E in these systems.

In the $PbCl_2 + MCl$ systems conductance minima in the $PbCl_2 + CsCl$ and $PbCl_2 + RbCl$ systems are deeper than that for the $PbCl_2 + KCl$ system, even though the difference in equivalent conductances of the component salts is much greater in the $PbCl_2 + KCl$ system. The $PbCl_2 + NaCl$ system has no minimum, although Λ_{NaCl} is much greater than Λ_{KCl}. The minimum of conductance is therefore not attributable to large differences between Λ for the pure components, as in the $LiCl + KCl$ system. In the $PbCl_2 + MCl$ systems the extent of formation of complex ions would increase in the sequence $Na^+ < K^+ < Rb^+ < Cs^+$, that is, in the same order as the numerical value of $-\Delta\Lambda^E$. Complex ions would be expected to be rendered unstable in the presence of highly polarizing Li^+.

Formulas for complex ions cannot be deduced from conductance results alone, but the activation energy maximum at $x_{KCl} = 0.8$ in Fig. 5-9 shows that bond breaking takes place as a preliminary to migration at this composition; hence, $PbCl_6^{4-}$ would appear to be an entity. $PbCl_3^-$ and $PbCl_4^{2-}$, which have been suggested also to explain other physical properties of the $PbCl_2 + MCl$ systems, may be formed in equilibrium with $PbCl_6^{4-}$—particularly at lower ratios of $MCl/PbCl_2$.

Systems with Positive Deviations from Additivity of Conductance

Figures 5-6 and 5-7 show equivalent conductance and molar volume of the system $CaCl_2 + MgCl_2$ against mole fraction. Similarly shaped isotherms are found for $PbCl_2 + CdCl_2$ and $CdCl_2 + BaCl_2$. In the absence of measurement of other physical properties of these systems, it is difficult to make structural deductions from the conductance and molar volume results, although a tentative explanation in terms of the increase of ionic character of one of the components, e.g., $CdCl_2$ in the $PbCl_2 + CdCl_2$ and $CdCl_2 + BaCl_2$ systems, has been proposed. This explanation requires that pure molten $CdCl_2$ be partly in the form of complex ions (or auto complexes), for example,

$$2CdCl_2 = Cd^{2+} + CdCl_4^{2-}$$

The addition of, for instance, $PbCl_2$ is assumed to dissociate the complexes, thus increasing conductance and, by increasing the efficiency of packing, causes ΔV^E to be negative. In this class of system, the phase diagram does not indicate the formation of intermediate compounds.

5-3 TRANSFERENCE NUMBER

Transference studies in pure molten salts are difficult both to carry out and to interpret theoretically because there is no solvent in the conventional sense; hence, another frame of reference is necessary. Transference cannot lead to concentration changes but only to a flow of the molten salt as a whole. For this reason the frame of reference is an external one—usually a sintered glass disk separating the salt into anode and cathode compartments—rather than the stationary solvent as in conventional solutions. For mixtures of molten salts, one salt is regarded as the solvent and measurements are made of the movement of the other with respect to the solvent salt.

Measurements in Pure Molten Salts

The main experimental difficulty is caused by the gravitational flow of salt from one compartment to the other, and early experiments conducted in cells with compartments separated by porous partitions were meaningless. The movement of melt by transference from one to the other compartment produced a gravitational back pressure that caused salt to flow back toward the initial position.

In an attempt to counteract back flow, Duke and Laity [9] used a conventional two-compartment cell, as shown in Fig. 5-10, connected not only by the usual sintered glass diaphragm but also by a capillary tube partly filled with molten salt but containing a nonconducting gas bubble to prevent conduction of electricity by this path. The movement of the gas bubble was used as a null detector to indicate when no transfer of matter was taking place by gravitational flow.

A small quantity of solid salt (e.g., $PbCl_2$) was added to one compartment. This tended to displace the bubble to one side and current was passed in such a direction as to counteract this tendency and to return the bubble to the original position. A knowledge of quantity of electricity

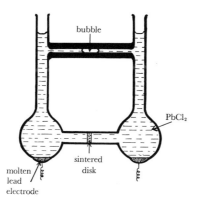

Fig. 5-10. *Bubble cell for determination of transference number (F. R. Duke and R. W. Laity, J. Phys. Chem., 59, 549 (1955)).*

needed to return the bubble to its starting position for the addition of a known weight of salt allows the calculation of transference number.

Another method, by Bloom *et al.*,[10] eliminated errors due to gravitational flow by sealing electrodes into the two horizontal compartments which were separated by a sintered disk and to which were sealed capillary tubes at either end. The whole collinear apparatus was adjusted so as to be perfectly horizontal by observing that no gravitational flow took place over an hour or more before passing current. The transfer of salt from one compartment to the other electrolytically was followed by observing the meniscus of the salt in one capillary during flow of current. The apparatus is shown in Fig. 5-11.

Various modifications of both main methods have been investigated. Other methods include the use of radio-tracers, emf of cells, and electrophoresis.

Many attempts have been made for theoretical analyses of transference number. Sundheim [11] derived the formula for transference number of ion A

$$t_A = \frac{M_B}{(M_A + M_B)} \tag{5-14}$$

by applying to transference the principle of conservation of momentum. On the other hand, Mulcahy and Heymann [12] related transference to ionic radius rather than mass and obtained the expression for uni-univalent salts

$$t_A = \frac{r_B}{(r_A + r_B)} \tag{5-15}$$

(M_A, M_B, are masses in atomic mass units and r_A, r_B, radii of ions A, B)

Correlations between experimental values of transference number and (5-14) are poor. Better agreement with experiment is reached when (5-15) is used, but even this equation is not entirely satisfactory, except for the alkali halides.

Some experimental cation transference numbers (t_+) are shown in Table 5-5, together with calculated values from Eqs. (5-14) and (5-15), respectively.

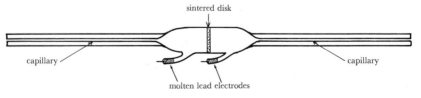

Fig. 5-11. *Capillary cell for determination of transference number (from Bloom and Easteal [10]).*

Table 5-5   *Cation Transference Numbers for Molten Alkali Salts*

Salt	Experimental t_+	Temperature (°C)	$\dfrac{M_-}{M_- + M_+}$	$\dfrac{r_-}{r_- + r_+}$
NaCl	0.62^a	860	0.59	0.66
	0.87^a	850		
KCl	0.62^a	830	0.48	0.58
	0.77^a	850		
KNO$_3$	0.60^a	350	0.61	0.63
AgNO$_3$	0.76^a	225–275	0.36	0.65
	0.75^b	232		

^{a} Duke *et al.*[13]
^{b} Bloom *et al.*[10]

Binary Mixtures

Modified Hittorf experiments have been used to determine the fraction of electricity carried by the component ions of a binary mixture. In these experiments, ionic conductances are unambiguously determined relative to the common ion of the opposite charge as a reference point.

In the AgNO$_3$ + NaNO$_3$ system the mobility (proportional to t_i/x_i) of each cation has been found to be constant over the whole composition range. Usually, however, the mobility of one cation is influenced by the other, and in the AgNO$_3$ + KNO$_3$ system the mobility of the cation of lesser concentration appears, on further dilution, to approach that of the cation of larger concentration.

Mobility measurements have not yielded definitive results on the presence of complex ions in such systems as PbCl$_2$ + MCl, although earlier results by relatively crude techniques tended to show the presence of complex ions in the PbCl$_2$ + KCl system. For the molten AlX$_3$ + NaX systems (X = F, Cl), negative transport numbers have been found for aluminum, thus providing convincing evidence for the presence of complex species. Similarly, in the molten ZnCl$_2$ + KCl and CdCl$_2$ + KCl systems the movement of Zn and Cd respectively, has been shown to take place towards the anode.

5-4   DIFFUSION

The measurement of coefficient of diffusion, or diffusivity, in molten salts is of great theoretical and practical importance, as this method has considerable value for structural determinations.

To measure diffusivities, non-steady state methods based on Fick's second law of diffusion are generally used. For diffusion occurring uni-directionally along the axis of a column of uniform cross section, this law may be expressed as

$$\frac{\partial C}{\partial t} = \frac{\partial}{\partial l}\left(D\,\frac{\partial C}{\partial l}\right) \qquad (5\text{-}16)$$

where C is the concentration of a certain component of the diffusion system, t the time of diffusion, D the diffusion coefficient, and l the distance along the axis. When D is independent of l or its variation with l is suffi-ciently small to be neglected,

$$\frac{\partial C}{\partial t} = D\,\frac{\partial^2 C}{\partial l^2} \qquad (5\text{-}17)$$

For certain specific initial and boundary conditions Eqs. (5-16) and (5-17) can be solved, giving C as a function of D, l, t, and if diffusion is arranged so that it has a definite initial concentration distribution and if the concentration distribution can be determined after time t, the diffusivity D can be calculated.

Many techniques for measurement in molten salts of self-diffusion coeffi-cients (i.e., for an ion in its own pure salt) have been utilized, mainly with the aid of isotopic tracers and capillaries to minimize convective mixing. They are mainly adaptations of techniques used for aqueous solutions. In one, a uniform bore capillary (1 mm diameter, 3–5 cm length), with an open end ground flat and the other end closed, is filled with an isotopically labeled salt and immersed vertically in a larger stirred volume of the same unlabeled salt, sufficiently large in volume that, after diffusion, the final tracer concentration in it is practically zero. The diffusion coefficients are obtained from a knowledge of the initial and final concentrations of the tracer in the capillary and the time of diffusion (Van Artsdalen et al.[14]). The most difficult step in the experiment is the filling of the capillary and its insertion into the liquid of larger volume without causing undue mixing.

Other techniques (e.g., Bockris and Hooper [15]) reverse the procedure. The labeled salt is in the bulk solution and its diffusion into a capillary of unlabeled salt is determined. This technique has been extended for use at high pressures. Yet other techniques measure the diffusion of a labeled salt along a capillary, while others use porous disks in which to carry out the diffusion.

Temperature Variation of Diffusion

Experimental results for self-diffusion of the individual ionic species in molten salts vary with temperature in accordance with the Arrhenius equation

$$D = D_\infty \exp\left(\frac{-E_D}{RT}\right) \tag{5-18}$$

where D_∞ is a constant and E_D is the activation energy for diffusion.

Table 5-6 gives diffusion coefficients and energies of activation for some molten salts. It is interesting to note that the energy of activation for diffusion is quite similar for anion and cation in the same molten salt.

The diffusion coefficients for the cation (D_+) for most salts so far investigated (the most notable exception being Na^+) are in the range 1–6 × 10^{-5} cm² sec⁻¹. The mean is about 3 × 10^{-5}, which is the same as the mean for room temperature liquids.

Relation between Diffusion Coefficient and Other Physical Properties

The diffusivity of an electrolyte in dilute aqueous solution can be thought as *diffusional mobility*. As concentration increases, diffusional mobility of a particular ion decreases and becomes more dependent on the nature of the other species present. Diffusional mobility has been related to *electrical mobility*, which is expressed in terms of the equivalent conductance of the solution. In an electrolyte solution the electrical mobility μ_i of an ion can be defined as

$$\mu_i = \frac{t_i \Lambda}{z_i \mathfrak{F}} \tag{5-19}$$

where t_i is its transference number, $\mathfrak{F}$ the faraday, z_i the charge on the ion, and Λ the equivalent conductance of the solution.

Table 5-6 *Diffusion Coefficients D, D_∞ and Energies of Activation for Diffusion E_D*

Salt	Temperature (°C)	Ion	$D \times 10^5$ (cm² sec⁻¹)	$D_\infty \times 10^3$ (cm² sec⁻¹)	E_D (cal mole⁻¹)
LiNO₃	350	Li⁺	2.93	2.47	5490 ± 110
	350	NO₃⁻	1.15	1.95	6340 ± 270
NaNO₃	350	Na⁺	2.33	1.29	4970 ± 80
	350	NO₃⁻	1.48	0.90	5080 ± 80
KNO₃	350	K⁺	1.52	1.32	5530 ± 200
	350	NO₃⁻	1.35	1.42	5760 ± 260
NaCl	838	Na⁺	9.62	3.32	7860 ± 110
	838	Cl⁻	6.73	3.02	8390 ± 40

Alternatively, the expression

$$\lambda_i = t_i \Lambda \tag{5-20}$$

is commonly used for ionic mobility (i.e., ionic conductance).

At infinite dilution the relationship between electrical and diffusional mobilities is

$$\frac{D_i}{RT} = \frac{\mu_i}{z_i \mathfrak{F}} \tag{5-21}$$

where R is the gas constant. Equation (5-21) is known as the *Nernst-Einstein equation* and is valid only at infinite dilution as, although D_i and μ_i both decrease with increasing concentration, their rate of decrease is not the same.

Attempts have been made to apply the Nernst-Einstein equation to molten salts which, although as concentrated as possible, behave in many respects (e.g., molar refractivity, conductance) in a similar manner to infinitely dilute electrolyte solutions. From (5-19), (5-20), and (5-21) the Nernst-Einstein equation can be shown to be

$$D_i = \frac{RT}{z_i^2 \mathfrak{F}^2} \lambda_i \tag{5-22}$$

Thus for an electrolyte such as molten NaCl

$$\Lambda = \frac{\mathfrak{F}^2}{RT} (D_{Na^+} + D_{Cl^-}) \tag{5-23}$$

Values of Λ calculated by means of Eq. (5-23) are as much as 40% too high and there is also general disagreement for other salts. Discrepancies increase with increasing temperature. Various explanations have been advanced for such discrepancies, mainly in terms of the coupled diffusion of anion and cation into paired vacancies, thus leading to diffusive migration of ions without carrying electric current (i.e., *currentless diffusion*).

Another equation in diffusion theory is the *Stokes-Einstein equation*

$$D_i = \frac{kT}{6\pi r_i \eta} \tag{5-24}$$

where r_i is the ionic radius, k the Boltzmann constant, and η the coefficient of viscosity.

The Stokes-Einstein equation would again be strictly applicable only at infinite dilution for an ion moving in a continuum, but is surprisingly effective in some cases. The relation between conductance and viscosity will be discussed in Section 5-5.

Theoretically, the ionic radii could be determined from Eq. (5-24), but as both D_i and η are temperature dependent in different ways, the numerical values of r_i so calculated are rather arbitrary. For highly conducting molten salts such as the alkali halides, however, ionic radii calculated by the Stokes-Einstein equation are always of the right order of magnitude—usually about 15%–50% less than the crystallographic radii for the same ions. This is good proof that the unit of transport in such molten salts is the simple ion rather than more complex species.

5-5 VISCOSITY

Viscosities of molten salts are of the same order of magnitude as room temperature liquids and liquid metals, that is, 0.005–0.05 P. Methods used for measurement are therefore modifications of the standard methods. For molten glasses and slags the values are many orders of magnitude higher, hence only special forms of the concentric cylinder method are applicable.

For molten salts the capillary method of Ubbelohde as modified by Bloom, Harrap, and Heymann [16] has had wide use. The cell is illustrated in Fig. 5-12.

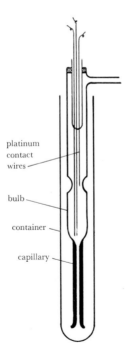

platinum
contact
wires

bulb

container

capillary

Fig. 5-12. *Capillary viscometer (from Bloom et al.*[16]*).*

The container is made of high melting glass and the capillary viscometer bulb has three platinum wires fixed in it, one at the top and two extending to the bottom. By means of a suitable bridge circuit the melt, on being drawn up into the viscometer bulb under reduced pressure, is made to close the electrical circuit between the bottom pair of wires, thus starting an electric clock, and on reaching the top contact causes the clock to stop, thus automatically recording the time for the viscometer bulb to fill under a known pressure. The dimensions of the bulb and the container tube are selected so that the melt levels in the container and bulb will be the same at half time. Since the head to be added to the driving pressure in the first half of the experiment is exactly counterbalanced by the head to be subtracted in the second half, pressure can be measured solely by an outside manometer. The capillary ends are trumpet shaped to avoid the application of the (Hagenbach) kinetic energy correction.

Many other methods have been applied successfully to molten salts. They include concentric cylinder methods, in which the torque on one cylinder (kept stationary) is measured while the other cylinder is rotated at a known rate. Oscillational methods and those involving velocity of fall of a spherical body in the melt have also been used.

Temperature Dependence of Viscosity

Viscosity decreases rapidly with increase of temperature. An exponential relation was first proposed by de Guzman and Dunn

$$\eta = A_\eta \exp \left(\frac{E_{\text{vis}}}{RT} \right) \qquad (5\text{-}25)$$

where A_η and E_{vis} are constants for any particular molten salt; E_{vis} is the energy of activation for viscous flow.

In the theory of absolute reaction rates, Eyring [17] arrived at an equation of similar form to (5-25) as follows:

$$\eta = 1.09 \times 10^{-3} \cdot \frac{M^{1/2} \cdot T^{3/2}}{V^{2/3} \cdot \Delta E_{\text{vap}}} \cdot \exp \left(\frac{E_{\text{vis}}}{RT} \right) \qquad (5\text{-}26)$$

In this equation ΔE_{vap} ($= \Delta H_{\text{vap}} - RT$) is the energy of vaporization. The preexponential term in Eq. (5-26) is practically independent of temperature, hence Eqs. (5-25) and (5-26) are essentially the same. The energy of activation for viscous flow is determined experimentally by plotting $\log_{10} \eta$ versus $1/T$; E_{vis} is the slope of the straight line thus obtained multiplied by 2.303 R. Values of η and E_{vis} for some molten salts are given in Table 5-7.

Table 5-7   *Viscosity and Energy of Activation of Viscous Flow* [a]

Salt	η (cP)	t (°C)	E_{vis} (kcal mole^{-1})
NaCl	1.02	900	9.1
KCl	1.13	800	7.4
AgCl	2.08	500	2.9
PbCl$_2$	2.22	650	6.7
CdCl$_2$	2.03	650	4.0

[a] From Harrap and Heymann.[18]

For molten halides Barzakowskii[2] and Bloom and Heymann[3] have shown that the energy (heat) of activation for viscous flow is always a factor of 2–3 times the heat of activation for conductance. This observation agrees with Frenkel's prediction based on the different mechanisms for the two processes. In electrical conduction Frenkel assumed that one particular ion may carry the bulk of the current, whereas in viscous flow both cation and anion need to move simultaneously to maintain electrical neutrality, thus requiring considerably larger energy barriers to be overcome. On the other hand the situation may be different for nitrate melts, where the ratio E_{vis}/E_κ is usually close to unity.

The difference in mechanism between conductance and viscosity can also be illustrated by the nonapplicability to molten salts of Walden's law.

$$\Lambda\eta = \text{constant} \qquad (5\text{-}27)$$

This law has been applied successfully to molten salts with large ions, such as the alkyl ammonium picrates, but does not apply to simple inorganic salts, such as halides. For most molten salts, it cannot be said, even qualitatively, that a decrease of viscosity leads to an increase of conductance, because in molten salt mixtures the conductances usually deviate from the ideal additive conductance isotherm in the negative direction and the viscosities of mixtures deviate also in the same direction.

Batchinski[18] and Macleod[18] showed theoretically that the viscosity of a liquid is controlled primarily by its free volume rather than the temperature (although free volume is again dependent on temperature). The Batchinski relation is

$$\eta = \frac{B}{(v - b)} \qquad (5\text{-}28)$$

where B and b are constants (b may be regarded as the incompressible volume) and v is the specific volume of the melt. Harrap and Heymann found that (5-28) applied very well to many different molten salts, e.g., $CdCl_2$, $CdBr_2$, $PbCl_2$, $AgCl$.

Viscosities of Mixtures of Molten Salts

The molten salt system $CdCl_2$ + $CdBr_2$ has a linear relation between viscosity and molar composition at a constant temperature. For all other binary systems so far investigated, the viscosity isotherms have negative deviations from linearity. There appears to be little or no correlation between the positions of minima in the viscosity isotherms and minima in those of conductance. Nor does there appear to be any correlation between energies of activation for conductance and viscosity.

The inferred formation of complex ions in molten salt systems appears to have no effect on the viscosity of the system. Hence in the $CdCl_2$ + KCl system, the shape of the conductance isotherm at 650°C with its pronounced minimum at about 0.6 mole fraction KCl and its maximum followed by a rapid decrease at 0.8 mole fraction KCl, has no counterpart in the 650°C viscosity isotherm, as shown in Fig. 5-13. It is relevant to note that in this system ΔV^E is positive, hence formation of complex ions would be accompanied by an increase of free volume, which would largely compensate for the effect of increasing the size of the unit of flow, as shown by the general validity of the Batchinski equation (5-28) for molten salts. Thus the viscosity isotherms for systems in which complex ions are formed (and which always have positive excess molar volumes) will always have the same general shape as those in which complex ions are not formed, but for which there is no increase of free volume on mixing.

5-6 THERMAL CONDUCTIVITY

The measurement of thermal conductivity, even for room temperature liquids, is difficult. Difficulties are multiplied for molten salts.

Three modes of heat transfer exist in liquids: (a) radiation; (b) convection, in which heat is transported as internal energy from one point to the other with the flowing medium; and (c) conduction, which is associated with transport of energy across the centers of the molecules on collision. In fluids, as distinct from solids, molecules are not confined to fixed positions, but constantly move even if the fluid as a whole is in a state of rest. Heat transported by this process is also included in the term thermal conductivity.

The property is very important practically, as molten salts are commonly used as heat transfer media, e.g., under the designation HTS (KNO_3 + $NaNO_2$ + $NaNO_3$ eutectic). The thermal conductivities of molten salts are 2–5 times higher than common organic heat transfer media, and their

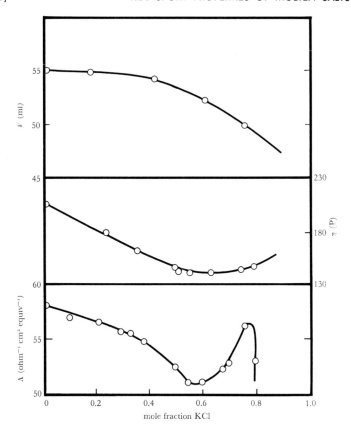

Fig. 5-13. *Isotherms of molar volume, viscosity, and equivalent conductance for the CdCl$_2$ + KCl system at 650°C (from Harrap and Heymann* [18]*).*

temperature coefficients are often small. The thermal stability of such media is also vastly superior to that of organic substances; hence molten nitrate mixtures can be used without decomposition to at least 500°C. Thermal conductivity is also very important theoretically, as it can be used to test theories of liquids.

Thermal conductivity $\mathcal{K}$ is defined as the quantity of heat flowing across unit area in unit time under unit gradient of temperature, and has been measured in molten salts by two main methods, steady state and transient. Turnbull [19] used a transient method to determine the thermal conductivities of a number of molten salts. In this method a thin platinum wire in the liquid is heated by a constant current and its rate of temperature rise is measured. Under suitable conditions the thermal conductivity may be evaluated from the rate of heat production and the temperature–time relation.

Bloom et al.[20] used a steady state method involving the transfer of heat (generated electrically) across a thin annulus of molten salt between two coaxial vertical silver cylinders. The thermal conductivity is given by

$$\mathcal{K} = \frac{Q \ln (r_2/r_1)}{2\pi l(t_1 - t_2)} \tag{5-29}$$

where Q is the quantity of heat flowing per second; r_1 the external radius of the inner cylinder; r_2 the internal radius of the outer cylinder; t_1, t_2 temperatures of inside and outside cylinders, respectively; and l the length of the molten salt annulus. Some values of thermal conductivity of molten salts are given in Table 5-8.

Thermal Conductivity and Free Volume

Kincaid and Eyring related the velocity of sound to thermal conductivity by the equation

$$\mathcal{K} = 2.80 \, \mathbf{k} n^{2/3} \gamma^{-1/2} U_L \tag{5-30}$$

where $\mathbf{k}$ is Boltzmann's constant, n the number of molecules in unit volume, $\gamma = C_p/C_v$, and U_L is the velocity of sound in the liquid. Equation (5-30) can be combined with an equation used by Bockris and Richards [21] to relate free volume V_f with velocity of sound.

$$V_f = \left[\frac{1}{U_L} \left\{ \frac{RT}{2(M_c M_a)^{1/2}} \right\}^{1/2} \right]^3 V \tag{5-31}$$

Here M_c, M_a = mass of cation and anion, respectively, and other symbols

Table 5-8   *Thermal Conductivities of Molten Salts*

Salt	Temperature (°C)	$10^3 \, \mathcal{K}$ (cal cm^{-1} sec^{-1} deg^{-1})
AgNO$_3$	300	1.30
KNO$_3$	393	1.30
NaNO$_3$	422	1.45
NaNO$_2$	314	1.70
HTS (KNO$_3$ 44%; NaNO$_2$ 49%; NaNO$_3$ 7% mole)	142	1.19

Table 5-9   *Free Volume for Molten Salts*

Salt	Temperature (°C)	V_f from (5-31) (ml mole^{-1})	V_f from (5-32) (ml mole^{-1})
NaNO$_3$	310	0.13	0.13
KNO$_3$	340	0.13	0.16
AgNO$_3$	310	—	0.12
NaNO$_2$	300	—	0.11

have their usual significance. Combining (5-30) and (5-31), we obtain

$$V_f = \left[\frac{2.80\ \mathbf{k}n^{2/3}}{\gamma^{1/2}\ \mathcal{K}} \left\{ \frac{RT}{2(M_c M_a)^{1/2}} \right\}^{1/2} \right]^3 V \tag{5-32}$$

which permits evaluation of V_f. Table 5-9 gives values of V_f calculated from (5-31) and (5-32).

Some binary molten salt systems have been investigated. In the AgNO$_3$ + KNO$_3$ system at 280°C, and probably also for AgNO$_3$ + NaNO$_3$ at 340°C, the relation between $\mathcal{K}$ and molar composition is approximately linear. For NaNO$_3$ + KNO$_3$ at 400°C, there is a minimum value of 0.9 in $\mathcal{K}$ at approximately 0.6 mole fraction KNO$_3$. The eutectic mixture (0.4 mole fraction KNO$_3$), which has a thermal conductivity of about 0.95 at 400°C, is a very suitable heat transfer salt.

REFERENCES

1. King, L. A., and Duke, F. R., *J. Electrochem. Soc.*, **111**, 712 (1964).
2. Barzakowskii, V. P., *Bull. Acad. Sci. USSR, Div. Chem. Sci.*, **5**, 47 (1941).
3. Bloom, H., and Heymann, E., *Proc. Roy. Soc.*, **A188**, 392 (1947).
4. Biltz, W., and Klemm, W., *Z. Anorg. Allgem. Chem.*, **152**, 267 (1926).
5. Markov, B. F., and Delimarskii, J. K., *Ukr. Khim. Zh.*, **19**, 255 (1953).
6. Mackenzie, J. D., and Murphy, W. K., *J. Chem. Phys.*, **33**, 366 (1960).
7. Van Artsdalen, E. R., and Yaffe, I. S., *J. Phys. Chem.*, **59**, 118 (1955); Yaffe, I. S., and Van Artsdalen, E. R., *J. Phys. Chem.*, **60**, 1125 (1956).
8. Bockris, J. O'M., Crook, E. H., Bloom, H., and Richards, N. E., *Proc. Roy. Soc.*, **A255**, 558 (1960).
9. Duke, F. R., and Laity, R. W., *J. Phys. Chem.*, **59**, 549 (1955).
10. Bloom, H., and Doull, N. J., *J. Phys. Chem.*, **60**, 620 (1956); Bloom, H., and James, D. W., *J. Phys. Chem.*, **63**, 757 (1959); Bloom, H., and Easteal, A. J., in *Electrochemistry*, p. 599, Pergamon, London, 1964.
11. Sundheim, B. R., *J. Phys. Chem.*, **60**, 1381 (1956).

12. Mulcahy, M. F. R., and Heymann, E., *J. Phys. Chem.*, **47**, 485 (1943).
13. Duke, F. R., and Bowman, A. L., *J. Electrochem. Soc.*, **106**, 626 (1959); Duke, F. R., and Cook, J. P., *J. Phys. Chem.* **62**, 1593 (1958); Duke, F. R., and Victor, G., *J. Electrochem. Soc.*, **110**, 91 (1963); Laity, R. W., and Duke, F. R., *J. Electrochem. Soc.*, **105**, 97 (1958).
14. Van Artsdalen, E. R., Brown, D., Dworkin, A. S. and Miller, F. J., *J. Am. Chem. Soc.*, **78**, 1772 (1956).
15. Bockris, J. O'M., and Hooper, G. W., *Disc. Faraday Soc.*, **32**, 218 (1961).
16. Bloom, H., Harrap, B. S., and Heymann, E., *Proc. Roy. Soc.*, **A194**, 237 (1948).
17. Eyring, H., in *The Theory of Rate Processes* by S. Glasstone, K. J. Laidler, and H. Eyring, p. 477, McGraw-Hill, New York, 1941.
18. Harrap, B. S., and Heymann, E., *Chem. Rev.*, **48**, 45 (1951).
19. Turnbull, A. G., *Aust. J. Appl. Sci.*, **12**, 30, 324 (1961).
20. Bloom, H., Doroszkowski, A., and Tricklebank, S. B., *Aust. J. Chem.*, **18**, 1171 (1965).
21. Bockris, J. O'M., and Richards, N. E., *Proc. Roy. Soc.*, **A241**, 44 (1957).

6

Optical Properties and Spectra of Molten Salts

Studies of optical properties of liquids have long been one of the most important physical methods for gaining structural information on such systems. The considerable experimental difficulties associated with such measurements on molten salts have, however, only recently been overcome.

Refractive index measurements, and more recently those of the Faraday effect, have played an important role in establishing the fundamentally ionic nature of molten salts. Raman and infrared spectra have been investigated to determine the vibrational frequencies of the fundamental modes of polyatomic ions, the presence of which has unambiguously been inferred in molten salts. Nevertheless uncertainties associated with the detailed interpretation of these spectra still remain. Ultraviolet and visible spectra give valuable information on the coordination and geometry of complexes in molten salt mixtures.

6-1 MOLAR REFRACTIVITY

The determination of refractive index n of molten salts leads to calculation of the molar refractivity R cm³ by means of the Lorentz-Lorenz equation

$$R = \frac{n^2 - 1}{n^2 + 2} \cdot \frac{M}{d} \qquad (6\text{-}1)$$

As molar refractivity is almost independent of temperature, it is a useful parameter for structural investigation of molten salts and their mixtures since the values for n extrapolated to infinite wavelength are directly related to the electron polarizability α of the medium by the relation

$$R = \left(\frac{4}{3}\right) \pi N \alpha \qquad (6\text{-}2)$$

where N is Avogadro's number.

R may be calculated for light of any wavelength by (6-1). The sodium D line and mercury green line have been most widely used for determination of refractive index of molten salts. If n is measured using sodium light, the resulting molar refractivity is R_D.

There have been only a few systematic investigations of refractive index of molten salts, presumably because of the considerable experimental difficulties involved. Most of the early work is unreliable. The first reliable investigation was of refractive index of molten alkali bromide + silver bromide systems by Thurmond,[1] who used a small hollow prism made of 1-mm-thick Vycor glass sheets and a spectrometer to determine angle of minimum deviation when the prism was filled with the molten salt. Refractive index at wavelength λ is given by

$$n_\lambda = \frac{\sin (\delta_\lambda + A)/2}{\sin A/2} \qquad (6\text{-}3)$$

where δ_λ is angle of minimum deviation at wavelength λ and A is the apex angle of the prism.

Zarzycki and Naudin[2] modified the method used by Thurmond. Their method, which is shown in Fig. 6-1, utilizes a solid base prism fixed on a goniometer platform with two vitreous silica plates clamped rigidly to two of the base-prism faces to form the prism angle of the upper prism, which holds the molten salt. The upper prism is made of thin platinum sheet, which acts as both an electrical heater and a container. It has two circular holes in positions covered by the silica plates for the light beam to enter and leave the melt. The angle of minimum deviation is measured in the usual manner for light of various wavelengths. Probable error is ± 0.001–0.01 in refractive index.

Bloom and co-workers[3] adapted a different method, making use of the "bent stick" principle, that is, the direct measurement of the path of a ray of light passing through the surface of the melt into the atmosphere above it. Two sets of cross hairs (platinum) rigidly fixed in the melt define the light path in the melt. A transit theodolite is used to measure the angles of incidence and refraction with illumination from below by light of a suitable wavelength. Accuracy is ± 0.001.

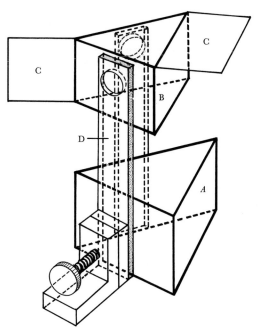

Fig. 6-1. *Cell for determination of refractive index of molten salts. A, metal prism (fixed on spectrometer platform); B, platinum heating crucible containing molten salt; C, heating current leads; D, silica window (from Zarzycki and Naudin [2]).*

Refractive index decreases in a linear manner with increase of temperature. Refractive index equations and molar refractivities are given for some molten salts in Table 6-1.

Table 6-1 *Refractive Index n and Molar Refractivity R_D for Molten Salts at Various Temperatures*

Salt	Temperature range (°C)	n_D (at Na D line) at t°C	R_D (cm³)
NaCl	810–885	$1.436 - 1.9 \times 10^{-4}\,(t - 700)$	9.48
KCl	785–835	$1.397 - 1.2 \times 10^{-4}\,(t - 700)$	11.60
NaNO₃	320–460	$1.495 - 2.0 \times 10^{-4}\,(t - 700)$	11.54
KNO₃	345–480	$1.473 - 1.7 \times 10^{-4}\,t$	13.57
PbCl₂	515–635	$1.995 - 2.3 \times 10^{-4}\,(t - 700)$	29.3
CdCl₂	625–725	$1.696 - 1.0 \times 10^{-4}\,(t - 700)$	21.3

As has been illustrated in Table 2-3, molar refractivity can be used to deduce the fundamentally ionic nature of molten salts. The difference in polarizabilities, $K^+ - Na^+$ is 2.21 cm³ for $R_D(KCl) - R_D(NaCl)$ at 850°C compared with 2.03 cm³ for $R_D(KNO_3) - R_D(NaNO_3)$ and 2.04 cm³ for $R_D(KNO_2) - R_D(NaNO_2)$ at 350°–400°C. These polarizability differences are similar to those for the infinitely dilute aqueous solutions of the ions. The refractivity difference $R_D(KNO_3) - R_D(KNO_2) = 1.90$ cm³ and $R_D(NaNO_3) - R_D(NaNO_2) = 1.91$ cm³. This represents the polarizability difference between O^{2-} in NO_3^- and $(e^-)_2$ in NO_2^-. The constancy of polarizability difference for ions in different pairs of salts shows that molar refractivity is an important structural parameter for molten salts and that every ion has a definite refractivity.

Molar Refractivities of Molten Salt Mixtures

For a binary mixture of x_1 mole fraction of a component of molecular weight M_1 and x_2 mole fraction of a component of molecular weight M_2 having density d

$$R_{mix} = \frac{n^2 - 1}{n^2 + 2} \cdot \frac{x_1 M_1 + x_2 M_2}{d} \tag{6-4}$$

For almost ideal systems, e.g., $NaNO_3 + KNO_3$, refractivity has been shown to obey the additivity relation

$$R_{add} = R_1 x_1 + R_2 x_2 \tag{6-5}$$

and the plot of R_{mix} against mole fraction is linear. In Fig. 6-2 the plots of R_D against mole fraction are shown for the systems $CdCl_2 + NaCl$ and $PbCl_2 + NaCl$. These are ideal systems as far as molar refractivity is concerned.

Figure 6-3 shows R_D as a function of mole fraction for the systems $CdCl_2 + KCl$ and $PbCl_2 + KCl$. The positive excess values of ΔR_D (i.e., $R_{mix} - R_{add}$) have been attributed by Bloom and Peryer [3] to the formation of complex ions in these systems, for example, $CdCl_3^-$, $CdCl_4^{2-}$, and $CdCl_6^{4-}$ in the $CdCl_2 + KCl$ system. The explanation of positive excess molar refractivities can be given in terms of generalizations due to Fajans, who showed that for neutral molecules the Lorentz-Lorenz equation gives satisfactory additivity values for mixtures. However, when electrical interactions are present, deviations from additivity take place. The Lorentz-Lorenz refraction gives a measure of looseness of the electronic system. It is tightened, i.e., refractivity is decreased, by adjacent positive charges, and loosened, i.e., refractivity is increased, by adjacent negative charges. When, within a given electronic system, the distribution of positive charges becomes less symmetrical, the refractivity is increased. The replacement of the rela-

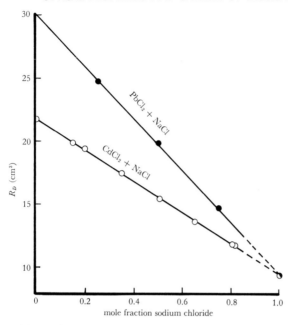

Fig. 6-2. *Molar refractivity of the molten salt systems* $CdCl_2 + NaCl$ *and* $PbCl_2 + NaCl$ *(at 750°C).* *(From H. Bloom and B. M. Peryer, Aust. J. Chem.,* **18,** *772 (1965).)*

tively uniform distribution of positive and negative ions in, say, $CdCl_2$ and KCl, respectively, by arrangements including complex ions, e.g., $CdCl_4^{2-}$, leads to a situation in which the distribution of positive and negative ions is less symmetrical and in which occur adjacent negative charges. Positive deviations from additivity of molar refractivity on mixing are therefore compatible with the formation of complex ions in the system. The lower polarizing power of K^+ allows the stability of complex ions in the $PbCl_2 + KCl$ and $CdCl_2 + KCl$ systems, but the higher polarizing power of Na^+ causes them to become less stable.

In the $AgBr + LiBr$ and $AgBr + RbBr$ systems, R_D appears to be an additive function of mole fraction, although the whole composition ranges were not investigated for any particular constant temperature. These systems are apparently relatively ideal.

Verdet Constant

Zarzycki and Naudin [2] have investigated the Faraday effect in molten salts, i.e., the rotation by means of a magnetic field, of the plane of polariza-

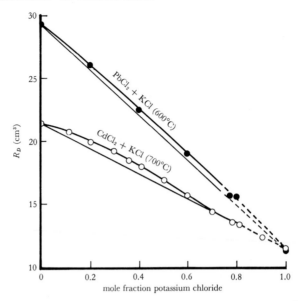

Fig. 6-3. *Molar refractivity of the molten salt systems $CdCl_2 + KCl$ (at 700°C) and $PbCl_2 + KCl$ (at 600°C). (R_{add} shown by straight lines.) (From H. Bloom and B. M. Peryer, Aust. J. Chem.,* **18,** *777 (1965).)*

tion of a polarized light beam passing through the medium. The angle of rotation θ is proportional to the length of the path l and the magnetic field intensity H in the direction of propagation; that is,

$$\theta = V \cdot H \cdot l \qquad (6\text{-}6)$$

where the constant of proportionality V is known as the *Verdet constant.* There is an analogous relation to molar refractivity (6-1) for the Verdet constant leading to a quantity known as the *molar magnetic rotation* Ω, which is given by the equation,

$$\Omega = \frac{n}{(n^2 + 2)^2} \cdot V \cdot \frac{M}{d} \qquad (6\text{-}7)$$

Ω is an additive property of ideal solutions in much the same manner as R, and the differences between Ω for different salts with a common ion is again always the same for the same pair of replacing ions. Thus

$$\Omega(\text{KCl}) - \Omega(\text{KF}) = 0.110$$

and

$$\Omega(\text{NaCl}) - \Omega(\text{NaF}) = 0.117$$
$$\Omega(\text{KBr}) - \Omega(\text{KF}) = 0.228$$

and

$$\Omega(\text{NaBr}) - \Omega(\text{NaF}) = 0.229$$

and so on.

6-2 ABSORPTION SPECTRA IN THE ULTRAVIOLET AND VISIBLE REGIONS

The wide application of the techniques of high temperature absorption spectrophotometry to the study of molten salt systems has proved to be of considerable assistance in establishing their detailed structure. The spectral region covered, 30,000–5000 cm^{-1}, allows investigation of electronic transitions at temperatures up to 1000°C. One advantage of molten salts as solvents in spectrophotometry is their great transparency to electromagnetic radiation over a wide range of frequency; hence, electronic transitions occurring in salts dissolved in suitable molten salt solvents can be measured without being masked by solvent absorption bands, as is often the case for room temperature solvents.

Technical problems associated with the modification of standard spectrometers for use in the high temperature region have largely been solved by rearrangement of the sequence of the various spectrometer components. The main problem in this adaptation is due to emission of radiation by the sample, sample compartment, and furnace. The normal arrangement for standard spectrophotometers is

Light source → Monochromator → Sample → Detector

and this is suitable up to 250°C, but above this temperature the signal-to-noise ratio rapidly diminishes owing to pick-up of the entire spectrum of radiation emitted by sample and furnace in addition to the transmitted monochromatic beam. Substantial gains in signal-to-noise ratio can be made by "chopping" the beam before passing into the heated sample or placing the monochromator after the sample; that is,

Light source → Sample → Monochromator → Detector

In this case the emitted radiation, except for that at the wavelength being measured, is rejected and the detector is able to function better. Various other arrangements and practical details for measurement have been described by Gruen.[4]

Electronic Spectra of Pure Salts

For the polyatomic anions, e.g., NO_3^-, (CrO_4^{2-}), in pure molten salts that have cations of noble gas electronic structure the electronic transitions are similar, except for normal thermal effects, to those observed in solids or in aqueous solution. One of the difficulties of working with molten salts is due to the high concentrations of the pure molten salts, and very thin films must be used to study the detail of the absorptions. Absorption coefficients at the maximum absorption are 10^4–10^5 per cm of sample light path for the alkali halides and a power of 10 less for alkali nitrates and thiocyanates. Every molten salt has an absorption edge and becomes virtually opaque to radiation of higher frequencies. The frequency of this absorption edge decreases by about 1000–2000 cm^{-1} (i.e., shift towards the red) for each 100° rise in temperature.

Smith and Boston [5] have comprehensively studied the spectra of molten nitrates, which have useful transitions corresponding to the excitation of a nonbonding electron largely localized on the oxygen atoms to an antibonding orbital, possibly π^*. The energy maximum of this band shows a progressive (blue) shift to higher frequencies as cation changes from Cs$^+$ through to Li$^+$. An explanation for this shift has been advanced in terms of the effect of cation field strength z_+/r_+ on the oppositely charged nitrate ions in regulating the nature of the excitation, which involves substantial transfer of charge from the oxygen periphery of the nitrate to an antibonding orbital, with a corresponding increase of electron density on the nitrogen atom. This charge transfer is opposed by the cation field, which increases in strength from Cs$^+$ to Li$^+$.

Electronic Spectra of Salt Mixtures

Investigations have largely been concerned with transition metal salts for which electronic transitions give characteristic spectra. The absorption spectra due to $3d$ transition metals are affected by their anionic environment and these effects can be explained by perturbations of the crystal field, since spin-orbit interactions are relatively small. The well-shielded $4f$ electrons in the lanthanide elements, together with the much greater spin-orbit coupling and temperature broadening of the transitions, make the study of effects of anions on the cation spectra in their molten salt solutions much more difficult.

Spectrum of Ti^{3+}

The spectrum of Ti^{3+} in chloride melts undergoes very large changes in band intensities and positions with change of temperature and mole fraction Cl$^-$ in the melt. In the LiCl + KCl eutectic at 400°C the spectrum of Ti^{3+} has a broad absorption band in the region 8000–15,000 cm^{-1} with a shoulder at 10,000 cm^{-1} and a maximum at 13,000 cm^{-1}. This is illustrated in Fig. 6-4, curve (a).   As temperature is increased a new band develops with a maximum at about 7000 cm^{-1} (curve b).   Intensity increases greatly with increase of temperature.   These spectral changes are considerably enhanced in a solvent composed of an equimolar mixture of CsCl and GaCl$_3$ [curves (c), (d), (e), and (f)].   Gruen and McBeth [4] explained these changes in terms of an equilibrium involving octahedral and tetrahedral coordinations

$$TiCl_6^{3-} = TiCl_4^- + 2Cl^- \qquad (6\text{-}8)$$

The transformation from octahedral $TiCl_6^{3-}$ to tetrahedral $TiCl_4^-$ results in a shift of the optical transition to lower energies and causes an increase of intensity due to change from distorted octahedral to distorted tetrahedral species lacking a center of inversion symmetry and displaying an appreciable degree of covalent bonding.   The effects of increasing temperature can be clearly seen in Fig. 6-4.

The effect of solvent on the transformation can be explained by the relative stability of the various complex ions that can be formed.   In the presence

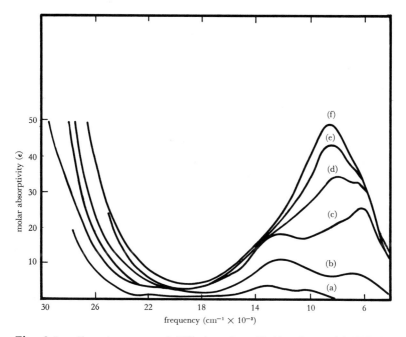

Fig. 6-4.   *Absorption spectra of Ti^{3+} in molten chloride solvents: (a) LiCl + KCl eutectic at 400°C; (b) LiCl + KCl eutectic at 1000°C; (c) CsGaCl$_4$ at 600°C; (d) CsGaCl$_4$ at 700°C; (e) CsGaCl$_4$ at 800°C; (f) CsGaCl$_4$ at 900°C.   (From Gruen and McBeth.[4])*

of CsCl + GaCl$_3$, the very stable complex species GaCl$_4^-$ is formed, thus lowering the Cl$^-$ activity compared with its activity in the LiCl + KCl solvent. The equilibrium reaction (6-8) is thus displaced in favor of TiCl$_4^-$.

Other Transition Metal Ions

The spectrum of V^{3+} is also very sensitive both to change of temperature and change of solvent. This has been interpreted by an octahedral–tetrahedral transformation equilibrium

$$VCl_6^{3-} = VCl_4^- + 2Cl^- \qquad (6-9)$$

The changes for V^{2+} have similarly been interpreted by the equilibrium between VCl$_6^{4-}$ and VCl$_4^{2-}$.

The spectrum of CoCl$_2$ in LiCl + KCl eutectic gives an absorption band partially resolved into two peaks. The spectrum is similar to the room temperature crystal spectrum of Co^{2+} substituted for Zn^{2+} in the CsZnCl$_4$ lattice in which Zn^{2+} is surrounded by 4Cl$^-$ in tetrahedral arrangement. The similarity of the Co^{2+} spectra in this crystal and in the melt suggests that the melt spectra are due to the CoCl$_4^{2-}$ complex ion. When Co^{2+} is substituted for Cd^{2+} in the octahedrally coordinated CsCdCl$_6$ lattice, an entirely different Co^{2+} spectrum is observed.

In LiCl + KCl eutectic, Mn^{2+} has spectra characterized by two absorption bands at approximately 22,000 cm^{-1} and 28,000 cm^{-1}. These spectra are not greatly sensitive to change of temperature between 400°C and 1000°C and are attributed to Mn^{2+} in tetrahedral coordination as MnCl$_4^{2-}$.

6-3 INFRARED AND RAMAN SPECTRA

Infrared and Raman spectra enable the vibrational modes of polyatomic species to be investigated and the main interest for molten salts is the identification of complex species in mixtures. Although there are difficulties in applying the techniques at high temperatures, valuable information has been obtained by them on the structure of molten salt systems. In the molecular spectra produced by transitions between vibrational and rotational energy levels, there are frequencies that correspond to these transitions. In infrared absorption spectra, these natural frequencies ν_i are obtained by direct measurement, but in Raman spectra the lines obtained are equal in frequency to the sums $\nu_0 \pm \nu_i$ where ν_0 is the frequency of the exciting radiation.

Raman Spectra

The most widely used experimental arrangement involves the use of the "Toronto" high intensity mercury vapor arc to excite Raman spectra.

The whole furnace and arc assembly can be contained in a transparent vacuum jacket to minimize heat losses and the spectra are measured by conventional Raman spectrometers.   In another method by Bues,[6] shown in Fig. 6-5, the surface of the liquid is used as a transparent interface for both entry and exit of the light beam.   The horseshoe-shaped mercury arc is situated above the vertical furnace in which the molten salt is held in a platinum crucible.   A well-formed silicon carbide crystal scatters the radiation from the arc and this passes through a slit into the spectrometer.   The method is very versatile and is very suitable for corrosive melts, but suffers from the disadvantage of a weak Raman spectrum owing to the relatively low intensity of the exciting radiation.

Infrared Spectra

Experimental difficulties are considerable in this field owing to the unavailability of suitably transparent windows that do not dissolve in molten salts; hence, methods that do not require the radiation to pass through the container are used.   In one method, the molten salt is suspended on a plati-

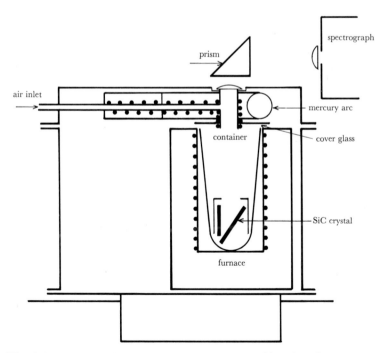

Fig. 6-5.   *Apparatus for Raman spectra of molten salts (from Bues [6]).*

num mesh screen; alternatively, a reflectance system is employed. Molten salts are highly absorbing; hence, very short light paths must be used.

Results from Vibrational Spectra

Pure salts. It is often feasible, by means of group-theoretical considerations, to distinguish the geometrical arrangement of atoms within a polyatomic species by observation of the number of vibrational bands observed in its infrared and Raman spectra. (Such a study has been made for the nitrate ion.) In highly symmetrical systems some vibrations may theoretically be active in either infrared or Raman spectra, but not in both. Degeneracy of vibrations may also limit the number of frequencies observed. On the contrary, there will be no degeneracy in systems of least symmetry and all vibrations will be active in both Raman and infrared. The number of vibrational frequencies observed in infrared and Raman spectra is thus governed by selection rules.

Selection rules apply strictly only to isolated species, hence to molecules in the vapor phase. In condensed systems, interactions between particles are often sufficient to cause splitting of degenerate frequencies and the appearance of forbidden vibrational bands. In molten salt systems, these factors will affect assignments of symmetry based solely on the number of active frequencies, and make conclusions regarding the geometry of polyatomic species in such systems rather inconclusive. Independent physical properties often need to be taken into account to supplement deductions from vibrational spectra in order to achieve unambiguous structural conclusions.

The nitrate ion. In the bonding of the planar NO_3^- there is a framework formed by the overlap of sp^2 hybrid orbitals on the nitrogen atom with p orbitals of the oxygen atom, and π bonds with considerable delocalization. NO_3^- may form a disklike species, by rotation about an axis through nitrogen perpendicular to the plane, or a spherical ion, by rotation about an axis through nitrogen in the plane of the disk. The vibrational spectra, however, indicate that rotation of the nitrate ion is restricted. NO_3^- has four fundamental vibrational frequencies and these have been investigated in aqueous solution and in the solid state as well as in the melt. The effect of the cation on the vibrational spectra of NO_3^- is particularly interesting and a summary for the alkali nitrates is given in Table 6-2.

Of the fundamental frequencies, ν_1 and ν_3 are the symmetric and antisymmetric stretching frequencies, respectively (both Raman active and strong in intensity), and are both decreased with increase of cation size. ν_1 is also present in the infrared spectrum, whereas it should be inactive. The out-of-plane bending frequency ν_2 increases as cation size increases, while the in-plane bending frequency ν_4 decreases with increase of cation size. The

Table 6-2   *Vibrational Spectra of Molten Nitrates* [a]

	Frequencies (cm^{-1})				
	ν_1	ν_2	ν_3	ν_4	Lattice mode
LiNO$_3$	1067	821	1375, 1460	726	343
NaNO$_3$	1053	827	1412	722	238
KNO$_3$	1048	829	1391	718	<220
RbNO$_3$	1046	—	1372	713	<220
CsNO$_3$	1043	—	1356	708	—

[a] From Wait and Janz.[7]

strong cation field of Li$^+$ removes the normal twofold degeneracy of the anti-symmetric stretching frequency ν_3 due to marked deformation of the NO$_3^-$ ion and results in a splitting of the band into two components.   Otherwise, no large differences are found between the melt frequencies and those in the solids or in the aqueous solutions.   The change of symmetric stretching frequency ν_1 with change of cation can be directly correlated with the free volume of the melt as calculated by the difference total volume minus hardcore volume.   The observed decrease of ν_1 during fusion is similarly explained by increase of free volume.   Obviously there are other factors than change of free volume that affect ν_1, as the expected decrease of ν_1 with increase of temperature is not observed experimentally.

The absorption bands observed in the infrared spectrum of the molten alkali nitrates at 343 cm^{-1} for LiNO$_3$, decreasing in frequency to < 220 cm^{-1} for KNO$_3$, have been assigned to latticelike vibrations in the melt and are presumably similar to the lattice vibrations of a crystalline solid.   Such vibrations in molten salts do not imply long-range order but are attributed to the strong short-range anion–cation interactions between the nitrate ions and their nearest neighbors.

Binary salt systems.   One of the earliest publications to shed light on the constitution of molten salt mixtures by Raman spectroscopy was that by Bues,[6] who used his reflection technique to investigate pure molten ZnCl$_2$ and CdCl$_2$, respectively, and their mixtures, with 0.33, 0.50, 0.67, and 0.80 mole fraction KCl.   In addition to the single characteristic Raman frequency for each pure salt, additional frequencies were found in mixture with KCl and these were assigned to ZnCl$_3^-$ and ZnCl$_4^{2-}$ in the ZnCl$_2$ + KCl system, and to CdCl$_3^-$ in the CdCl$_2$ + KCl system.   For the zinc complexes, the difference in frequencies assigned was only small, hence Bredig and Van Artsdalen [8] reexamined Bues's data with the conclusion that the single complex $ZnCl_4^{2-}$ or $CdCl_4^{2-}$ was equally consistent with the measured spectra in each system.

There have been several recent investigations of Raman spectra of pure molten $ZnCl_2$ and the $ZnCl_2 + KCl$ system. They are summarized by Moyer, Evans, and Lo.[9] In molten $ZnCl_2$ there are five bands, an intense polarized band at 226 cm^{-1} and other weaker bands. The effect of increase of temperature is to increase the intensity of a weak band at 305 cm^{-1}, but increased temperature has no effect on those at 226 and 250 cm^{-1}. The bands have been assigned to various vibrational modes of the $(ZnCl_2)_n$ polymer, and the changes in spectrum with change of temperature can be well explained in terms of the progressive depolymerization as temperature is increased. The $(ZnCl_2)_n$ network is regarded as being composed of $ZnCl_4$ tetrahedra joined at the corners to give a three-dimensional array as in Fig. 2-8. Even at 500°C, however, the spectra show that the vast majority of ZnCl bonds are bridging rather than terminal; hence, the network is quite stable several hundred degrees above the freezing point.

In chloride-rich solutions with KCl, the Raman frequencies of $ZnCl_2$ change considerably, as shown in Table 6-3.

The bridging Zn–Cl stretching frequencies of polymeric $ZnCl_2$ are reduced in intensity and the weak band at 250 cm^{-1} disappears on the first addition of KCl. The intense polarized band at 226 cm^{-1} gradually diminishes, while the terminal Zn–Cl stretching bands at 305 and 360 cm^{-1} in pure $ZnCl_2$ are shifted to lower frequencies and become first more intense, then diminish. This pattern is obscured in the case of the 305-cm^{-1} band by the spectrum of $ZnCl_4^{2-}$, which gradually emerges and becomes apparent in the $2ZnCl_2\cdot3KCl$ and $ZnCl_2\cdot2KCl$ mixtures.

All the observations can be explained by depolymerization of $(ZnCl_2)_n$ on addition of KCl by the reaction

$$(ZnCl_2)_n + Cl^- \rightarrow (ZnCl_2)_{n-m} + (ZnCl_2)_m \cdot Cl^- \qquad (6\text{-}10)$$

Table 6-3 *Observed Bands (cm^{-1}) in Raman Spectra of Molten Mixtures* [a]

$ZnCl_2$	$4ZnCl_2\cdot KCl$	$2ZnCl_2\cdot KCl$	$ZnCl_2\cdot KCl$	$2ZnCl_2\cdot3KCl$	$ZnCl_2\cdot2KCl$
75 ± 8, w	80 ± 8, w	75 ± 8, w	80 ± 8, w	70 ± 8, w	75 ± 8, w
			125 ± 10, w	120 ± 5, w	124 ± 5, w
226 ± 10, s, p	226 ± 8, s, p	226 ± 8, s, p	218 ± 5, vw		
250 ± 10, w					
305 ± 10, w	288 ± 5, w, p	290, m, p	292 ± 5, m, p	294 ± 5, s, p	283 ± 3, s, p
360 ± 10, w	349 ± 5, m, p	344 ± 8, w, p			

[a] From Moyer, Evans, and Lo.[9] Letter symbols in table mean: p, polarized; w, weak; vw, very weak; m, medium; s, strong. All bands are broad.

and this process continues in steps upon further addition of KCl until a molar ratio $ZnCl_2:KCl$ of 4:1. On adding further KCl the reaction

$$(ZnCl_2)_m \cdot Cl^- + Cl^- = ZnCl_4^{2-} + (ZnCl_2)_{m-1} \qquad (6\text{-}11)$$

begins to predominate. The complete breakup of the $(ZnCl_2)_n$ polymeric network to form $ZnCl_4^{2-}$ takes place as the molar ratio of KCl to $ZnCl_2$ is increased toward 1:1. The bands in the $2ZnCl_2 \cdot 3KCl$ and $ZnCl_2 \cdot 2KCl$ mixtures are those of the $ZnCl_4^{2-}$ complex ion. In the Raman data there is still the possibility that the $ZnCl_2$ monomer and $ZnCl_3^-$ may also be present in the pure salt and its mixtures with KCl. Figure 2-8 illustrates the degradation of the polymeric $ZnCl_2$ structure into smaller polymeric sections and the simpler species $ZnCl_4^{2-}$, $ZnCl_3^-$, $ZnCl_2$, $ZnCl^+$, Zn^{2+}, and Cl^-.

The formation of complex ions was clearly demonstrated by Janz and James [10] by Raman spectroscopy for mixtures of $HgCl_2$ with KCl or NH_4Cl. In addition to the characteristic Raman spectrum of $HgCl_2$ (present as undissociated molecules), they observed frequencies assigned to $HgCl_3^-$ and $HgCl_4^{2-}$, neither of which is known in solid double salts. Much work has also been carried out on Ga^{2+} and Ga^{3+} halides and their mixtures by Woodward et al.[11] using Raman spectroscopy. In the molten state neither GaX_2 nor the polymer $(GaX_2)_n$ were found to be present in pure $GaCl_2$ or $GaBr_2$, but the complex ion GaX_4^- was present. Hence molten gallium halides are constituted of Ga^+ (oxidation state I) and GaX_4^- (oxidation state III). In molten mixtures of $GaCl_3$ and NaCl, Raman spectra show the presence of a mixture of Ga_2Cl_6 and $GaCl_4^-$ rather than only the complex halide as in Ga(II) salts.

An interesting study of the systems $AlCl_3 + NaCl$ and $AlCl_3 + KCl$ by Raman spectroscopy has recently been published by Balasubrahmanyam and Nanis [12] following earlier work on these systems by others. Part of the Raman spectrum of the molten equimolar mixture $AlCl_3 \cdot KCl$ at 300°C is shown in Fig. 6-6. In the whole of the spectrum there are nine Raman frequencies, one very intense at 353 cm^{-1}, three of medium intensity at 182, 196, and 508 cm^{-1}, and five that are weak or very weak. Five of the lines are depolarized. The spectrum of solid $AlCl_3 \cdot KCl$ also has substantially the same nine Raman frequencies. The results are explained by the formation of the complex species $AlCl_4^-$ of distorted tetrahedral structure in both solid and molten $AlCl_3 \cdot KCl$. In the $AlCl_3 \cdot NaCl$ spectrum there were only four Raman frequencies, one very intense at 349 cm^{-1}, two of medium intensity at 145 and 183 cm^{-1}, and one at 580 cm^{-1}, very weak. Only the 349-cm^{-1} line is polarized. The results are consistent with the formation of $AlCl_4^-$ of regular tetrahedral structure in the melt. The difference between spectra of $AlCl_3 \cdot KCl$ and $AlCl_3 \cdot NaCl$ was explained in terms of difference in tendencies of Na^+ and K^+ to associate with the complex ions.

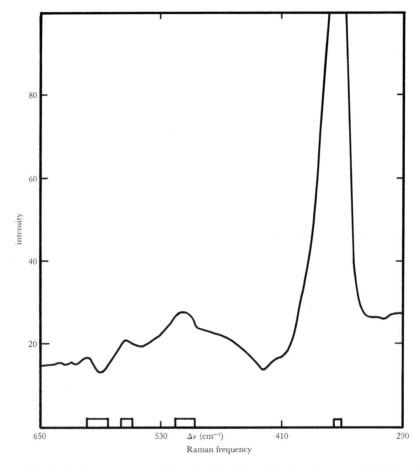

Fig. 6-6. *Raman spectrum of liquid AlCl₃·KCl at 300°C in the region 290–650 cm⁻¹ (excitation 4358 Å) (from Balasubrahmanyam and Nanis* [12]).

6-4 NUCLEAR MAGNETIC RESONANCE SPECTRA

This technique has not been widely applied to molten salts, although the isotope ^{205}Tl is favorable for NMR studies. In an assembly designed by Schoolery and Roberts, a hot air stream heats a sample holder without heating the cross-coil spectrometer head. The method is suitable to 300°C.

Hafner and Nachtrieb [13] measured the chemical shifts of ^{205}Tl thallium(I) halide + alkali halide in molten binary mixtures relative to a provisional standard probe containing an aqueous Tl⁺ solution. The measurements were limited to 720°C by the furnace and probe design, but temperatures up to 1000°C should be feasible.   The NMR spectra showed that the resonance frequency of $^{205}Tl^+$ varies in a linear manner with mole fraction of added alkali halide.   The direction of the chemical shift (δ), which is shown in Fig. 6-7, depends on the radius of the alkali cation, being upfield for the highly polarizing Li^+ and Na^+, but downfield for K^+, Rb^+, and Cs^+, relative to pure TlCl.   The change of slope of the chemical shift versus mole fraction MCl is in the sequence Li^+, Na^+, K^+, Rb^+, Cs^+ and the order is the same for the bromides and iodides as additives to the corresponding thallium(I) salt. For a given mole fraction of alkali halide, δ_{Tl} is a linear function of alkali cation radius.

A simple calculation shows that the electrostatic deformation of Tl^+ by the field of the foreign cation in a next-nearest-neighbor position is much too small to account for the effect of this added cation on the chemical shift, and in any event the sign of the observed effect is opposite to that which would be expected from deformation of Tl^+.   The explanation proposed by Hafner and Nachtrieb was in terms of the increased probability for the formation of a Σ^+ Tl—X bond in the melt as a consequence of the addition of MX, with

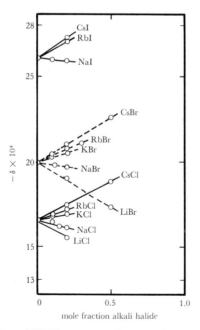

Fig. 6-7.   *Dependence of $^{205}Tl^+$ chemical shift in thallium halide $+$ alkali halide binary systems.   Chlorides and bromides at 520°C; iodides at 500°C (from Hafner and Nachtrieb [13]).*

the formation of complex species. The covalent interaction between Tl^+ and X^- is decreased by alkali ions of small radius and increased by those of large radius. This is similar to the explanation proposed in Section 5-2 to explain the effect of different alkali cation radii on equivalent conductance of the molten salt systems $PbCl_2 + MCl$ and $CdCl_2 + MCl$ (M = Li, Na, K, Rb, Cs).

One of the important features of NMR as a method of establishing the presence of complex ions in molten salts is the relatively long time of observation ($\sim 10^{-7}$ sec). This is long enough to allow an averaging out of the ion motions in the liquid but short enough to see complex entities.

6-5 THE FORMATION OF COMPLEX IONS IN MOLTEN SALT MIXTURES

Spectral investigations offer one of the most direct methods of demonstrating the existence of complex ions in molten salts and provide as complete a collection of evidence for the formation of such species as are available for room temperature systems. Molten salt systems do, however, differ from those involving "inert" solvents in several ways, the most obvious being that in molten salt solvents with a common anion, the ions that are used as ligands are also present as solvent. For this reason the exact formulas of complex ions are usually harder to determine in molten salt solvents than in, say, water. The use of molten salt solvents with no ions in common would approximate more closely to an inert solvent, and for this reason the results from cryoscopic determinations must be given considerable weight when attempting to establish their formulas.

It is difficult to see how the physical chemistry of many molten salt systems could be explained in any manner other than that requiring the formation of complex ions. Nevertheless, many investigators are reluctant to accept this and will go to extremes to advance other explanations for observed properties. In a very useful book on the thermodynamics of molten salt systems, Lumsden [14] relies heavily on regular solution theory, and proceeds empirically to evaluate the parameter b in the regular solution Eqs. (4-22) and (4-23) from measured thermodynamic data. In some systems it is difficult to assign a constant adjustable parameter b, but generally this method has value from the practical viewpoint insofar as it enables the presentation of equations from which reasonably accurate values of thermodynamic activities in molten salt systems can be calculated at required mole fractions. The method fails when an attempt is made to extend its utility to other physical properties. Intuitively it is not pleasing as it attempts to describe the behavior of all molten salt systems in terms of simple electrostatic interactions and London forces only, and results in the formulation of, for example, a molten mixture of Li_2O and SiO_2 as Li^+, Si^{4+}, and O^{2-}. This is in violent disagreement with the results of virtually all known physical properties of this and other molten salt systems.

In most cases the formulas of complex ions attributed to molten salt solutions are those that are accepted complexes in aqueous solution or in crystals of known structure, either pure or in dilute solid solution. It is not relevant that complex ion stoichiometry and stability can be qualitatively accounted for by crystal field or other electrostatic considerations, as opposed to covalent bonding, as the same factors also appear to be equally important in accounting for complexes in inert solvents or in solids.

One of the problems in molten salt chemistry is to advance criteria for predicting the formation of complex ions in a particular system. In an attempt to solve this problem, correlations have been made with compounds

Table 6-4   *Systems in Which Complex Ions Are Formed*

System	Method of investigation	Complex ions postulated
$KCl + CdCl_2$	Conductance, molar volume, Raman spectra, emf, vapor pressure, cryoscopy, heat of mixing	$CdCl_3^-$ $CdCl_4^{2-}$ $CdCl_6^{4-}$
$KCl + ZnCl_2$	Conductance, Raman spectra, emf	$ZnCl_3^-$ $ZnCl_4^{2-}$
$KCl + PbCl_2$	Conductance, molar volume, transport number, surface tension, emf, vapor pressure	$PbCl_3^-$ $PbCl_4^{2-}$ $PbCl_6^{4-}$
$KCl + MgCl_2$	Conductance, molar volume, activity, heat of mixing	$MgCl_4^{2-}$
$KCl + CuCl$	Conductance	$CuCl_3^{2-}$
$KF + ZrF_4 (+ NaF)$	Vapor pressure, IR spectra	ZrF_5^-
$KI + CdI_2$	Conductance, molar volume	CdI_4^{2-}
$RbCl + PbCl_2$	Emf, surface tension, conductance, molar volume	$PbCl_3^-$ $PbCl_4^{2-}$ $PbCl_6^{4-}$
$CsCl + CoCl_2$	UV absorption spectra	$CoCl_4^{2-}$
$CsCl + NiCl_2$	UV absorption spectra	$NiCl_4^{2-}$
$CsCl + CuCl_2$	UV absorption spectra	$CuCl_4^{2-}$
$CsCl + NpCl_4$	UV absorption spectra	$NpCl_6^{2-}$
$CsCl + PbCl_2$	Conductance, molar volume	$PbCl_3^-$ $PbCl_4^{2-}$ $PbCl_6^{4-}$
$KF + AlF_3$ and $NaF + AlF_3$	Conductance, surface tension, cryoscopy, Raman spectra	AlF_4^-

that crystallize out of the molten mixtures as intermediate phases. On these grounds it can be predicted that there is little likelihood of complex ion formation in molten $PbCl_2$ + NaCl (Fig. 4-1) and NaCl + KCl (Fig. 4-2), but that complex ions are very likely in molten $CaCl_2$ + KCl (Fig. 4-3), $PbCl_2$ + KCl (Fig. 4-4), $PbCl_2$ + RbCl (Fig. 4-5), and NaF + AlF_3 (Fig. 4-6). Although there is a considerable weight of evidence to suggest that the formation of solid intermediate phases does in fact indicate that complex ions are likely to be formed in the molten mixtures from which they crystallize, there is also much contrary evidence to suggest that an exact correspondence between complexes in solid and melt is unlikely. In many molten salts, e.g., HgX_2 + KX systems, the complex ions established by physical methods have no counterpart in the solid. The establishment of the conditions of formation, and the structure of complex ions in molten salts, will be the most important aspect of research in this subject in the near future.

Some molten salt systems in which there is good evidence for the formation of complex ions are shown in Table 6-4. This list is by no means exhaustive.

REFERENCES

1. Thurmond, C. D., *J. Am. Chem. Soc.*, **75,** 3928 (1953).
2. Zarzycki, J., and Naudin, F., *Rev. Hautes Temp. Refract.*, **1,** 121 (1964).
3. Bloom, H., and Rhodes, D. C., *J. Phys. Chem.*, **60,** 791 (1956); Bloom, H., and Peryer, B. M., *Aust. J. Chem.*, **18,** 772 (1965).
4. Gruen, D. M., in *Fused Salts*, (B. R. Sundheim, ed.), p. 301, McGraw-Hill, New York, 1964; Gruen, D. M. and McBeth, R. L., *Rev. Pure Appl. Chem.*, **6,** 23 (1963).
5. Smith, G. P., in *Molten Salt Chemistry* (M. Blander, ed.), p. 427, Interscience, New York, 1964.
6. Bues, W., *Z. Anorg. allgem. Chem.*, **279,** 104 (1955).
7. Wait, S. C., and Janz, G. J., *Quart. Rev.*, **17,** 225 (1963).
8. Bredig, M. A., and Van Artsdalen, E. R., *J. Chem. Phys.*, **24,** 478 (1956).
9. Moyer, J. R., Evans, J. C., and Lo, G. Y-S., *J. Electrochem. Soc.*, **113,** 158 (1966).
10. Janz, G. J., and James, D. W., *J. Chem. Phys.*, **38,** 905 (1961).
11. Woodward, L. A., Garton, G., and Roberts, H. L., *J. Chem. Soc.*, p. 3723 (1956); Woodward, L. A., Greenwood, N. N., and Worrall, I. J., *J. Chem. Soc.*, p. 1505 (1958).
12. Balasubrahmanyam, K., and Nanis, L., *J. Chem. Phys.*, **42,** 676 (1965).
13. Hafner, S., and Nachtrieb, N. H., *J. Chem. Phys.*, **42,** 631 (1965).
14. Lumsden, J., *The Thermodynamics of Molten Salt Mixtures*, Academic Press, London, 1966.

7

Salt Vapors

Detailed attention to the constitution of salt vapors began after 1950. Prior to that it was assumed, following the classical molecular weight determinations for salt vapors by Nernst, that they were composed of simple unassociated molecules. A study of salt vapor systems has considerable practical importance, as vaporization processes account for material losses in many high temperature preparative processes (e.g., electrolytic extraction of aluminum). Conversely, vaporization processes may be made use of for the preparation of certain compounds. From the theoretical point of view, an investigation of salt vapors has considerable interest both for an explanation of forces of interaction and in the investigation of the formation of complex species, the presence of which is now well established in most salt vapors so far investigated.

The process of vaporization and the structure of salt vapors have been investigated by many methods. Molecular beam resonance and velocity distribution experiments have been used to advantage, although the application of mass spectrometry has yielded more direct information. The measurement of vapor pressure by two independent methods, e.g., by boiling point and transpiration, respectively, has allowed the investigation of complex equilibria in the vapor phase over usefully wide ranges of temperature and pressure.

7-1 VAPOR PRESSURES OF PURE SALTS

Vapor pressure measurement has been discussed in Section 4-6. Results are usually expressed as a function of temperature by making use of the Clapeyron equation

$$\frac{dP}{dT} = \frac{\Delta H_{vap}}{T \Delta V} \tag{7-1}$$

where ΔH_{vap} is the heat of vaporization to the real vapor, assumed to be constant over a range of temperature, and ΔV is the increase of volume from the liquid to the real vapor, per mole.

Equation (7-1) can easily be transformed to the form

$$\frac{d \ln P}{dT} = \frac{\Delta H_{vap}}{RT^2} \tag{7-2}$$

In Eq. (7-2) the ideal gas law is assumed to apply—an assumption that has been demonstrated to be valid for salt vapors at pressures below 1 atm.

The use of (7-2) allows the ready calculation of heat of vaporization and on integration yields an equation of the form

$$\log_{10} P = A - \frac{B}{T} \tag{7-3}$$

If ΔH varies with temperature, the equation

$$\log_{10} P = - \left(\frac{\Delta H_0}{2.303\,RT} \right) + \left(\frac{\Delta C_p}{2.303\,R} \right) \log_{10} T + I \tag{7-4}$$

where ΔC_p is the heat capacity of the vapor minus that of the liquid (i.e., ΔC_p is usually negative) and I is an integration constant, is used. Equation (7-4) follows from Eq. (7-2) and the temperature variation of ΔH_{vap} (cf. (4-48)). Equation (7-4) leads to the three-term vapor pressure equation

$$\log_{10} P = A - \frac{B}{T} - C \log_{10} T \tag{7-5}$$

Some vapor pressure equations and heats of vaporization of molten salts are given in Table 7-1.

Polymerization Equilibria in the Vapor Phase above Molten Salts

For aluminum chloride, the vapor is well known to consist almost entirely of the dimer Al_2Cl_6, but for the alkali halides the dimerization reaction

$$2MX = (MX)_2 \tag{7-6}$$

Table 7-1   *Vapor Pressure and Heat of Vaporization of Some Pure Molten Salts*

Salt	$\log_{10}$ P (mm) at $T°K$	ΔH_{vap} (kcal mole^{-1})
NaCl	$20.929 - 11,495/T - 3.526 \log_{10} T$	$52.6 - 7.0 \times 10^{-3}T$
KCl	$20.798 - 11,023/T - 3.526 \log_{10} T$	$50.4 - 7.0 \times 10^{-3}T$
AgCl	$8.5974 - 10,385/T$	47.5
CdCl$_2$	$8.5371 - 6929/T$	31.7
PbCl$_2$	$31.726 - 10,168/T - 6.65 \log_{10} T$	$46.5 - 1.32 \times 10^{-2}T$

is usually incomplete but becomes more complete in the sequence CsX $<$ RbX $<$ KX $<$ NaX $<$ LiX. For lithium chloride most of the vapor is present as (LiCl)$_2$ with some as (LiCl)$_3$ and (LiCl)$_4$. Relatively little monomer exists. In sodium chloride there is a large proportion of (NaCl)$_2$ in the vapor but monomeric NaCl is also an important species. For such an equilibrium at a fixed temperature the equilibrium constant K can be expressed in terms of the degree of association α and the total vapor pressure P atm as follows.

$$K = \frac{\alpha(1 - \alpha/2)}{2P(1 - \alpha)^2} \quad \text{atm}^{-1} \tag{7-7}$$

Since

$$\frac{\text{Apparent molecular weight of the vapor}}{\text{Formula weight of the monomer}} = \frac{1}{(1 - \alpha/2)} \tag{7-8}$$

the degree of association can be calculated over a wide range of temperature provided the apparent molecular weight can be measured. To determine α and K, the boiling point method can be used to measure actual vapor pressure absolutely, and a transpiration method is used to calculate apparent molecular weight (Section 4-6). The results of such calculations for NaCl and KCl agree reasonably with similar determinations by mass spectrometry. The vapor pressure method is capable of use from about 3 mm to 760 mm. At 624°C and 10^{-2} mm, KCl vapor consists of 19% dimeric species and 81% monomer, while NaCl vapor at 647°C and 10^{-2} mm consists of 62% (NaCl)$_2$ and only 38% NaCl monomer.

High temperature mass spectrometry has been widely used to study the dimerization equilibria, but in this method the vapor pressures to be studied must be low—often between 10^{-10} and 10^{-6} atm. A Knudsen cell is used to produce the vapor, which effuses into the room temperature, low-pressure chamber of the mass spectrometer where it is ionized by electron impact. As the upper limit of pressure in the effusion cell is about 10^{-4} atm, this places an upper limit also on temperature at which the condensed phase may be studied. Various decompositions are possible under electron impact; for example, for lithium fluoride

$$LiF + e^- = LiF^+ + 2e^-$$
$$LiF + e^- = Li^+ + F + 2e^-$$
$$(LiF)_2 + e^- = Li_2F^+ + F + 2e^-$$
$$(LiF)_2 + e^- = LiF^+ + LiF + 2e^-$$
$$(LiF)_2 + e^- = Li^+ + LiF + F + 2e^- \quad \text{etc.}$$

Parent ions of polymeric alkali halides have very low stability; hence equilibrium partial pressures are determined usually from the intensities of the mass peaks of the corresponding fragment ions. Care must be taken to avoid the recording of ions that are formed by other processes, e.g., by ion–molecule reactions. An investigation of appearance potentials is very helpful in this respect.

In a mass spectrometer the ratio of partial pressure of monomer P_1 to that of dimer P_2 is given in terms of the corresponding ion currents

$$\frac{P_1}{P_2} = \frac{I_1 \, \sigma_2 S_2}{I_2 \, \sigma_1 S_1} \tag{7-9}$$

where σ_1, σ_2 are the ionization cross sections; S_1, S_2 the ion detection efficiencies. These quantities can be computed for given ions.

Heats of Dimerization

The standard heats of formation of the solid alkali halides and their monomeric vapors have been reviewed by Brewer and Brackett.[1] Heats of association of monomer to form dimeric species, i.e., for the reactions $2MX(g) = (MX)_2(g)$, have been computed from variation of the constant K in Eq. (7-7) with change of temperature, by means of the van't Hoff equation

$$\frac{d \ln K}{dT} = \frac{\Delta H_D}{RT^2} \quad \text{i.e.,} \quad \frac{2.303 \, R \, d(\log_{10} K)}{d(1/T)} = -\Delta H_D \tag{7-10}$$

Some values of heats of dimerization are given in Table 7-2 for alkali chloride vapors. They are strongly exothermic.

7-2 MIXED HALIDES

The presence of mixed halides in the vapor can sometimes be inferred from measurements of thermodynamic activity. The activities of $PbBr_2$ in molten mixtures of $PbCl_2$ were measured by Salstrom and Hildebrand [2] by emf's of formation cells. The activities were lower than the Temkin ideal mixture values for all compositions. Greiner and Jellinek [3] subsequently

Table 7-2   *Heat of Dimerization* (ΔH_D)

Salt	$T°K$	$-\Delta H_D$ (kcal mole^{-1} dimer)	Method
LiCl	800	50.1	Mass spectrometry
	800	49.1	Mass spectrometry
NaCl	920	46.4	Molecular beam
	930	44.7	Mass spectrometry
	930	51.8	Vapor density
	1300	50.6	Vapor density
KCl	897	47.6	Molecular beam
	900	41.5	Mass spectrometry
	900	41.7	Vapor density
	1300	43.8	Vapor density

investigated the activities of both $PbCl_2$ and $PbBr_2$ by vapor pressure measurements (cf. Section 4-6). Whereas a_{PbBr_2} was less than the ideal value for all compositions, the apparent values of a_{PbCl_2} were mostly higher than ideal and this is contrary to the Gibbs-Duhem relationship (4-8). The explanation advanced by Greiner and Jellinek was that a reaction to form the double molecular species $PbCl_2 \cdot PbBr_2$ took place in the vapor phase, thus making the apparent vapor pressure of both $PbCl_2$ and $PbBr_2$ too high. They were able to calculate an equilibrium constant for the assumed reaction. Subsequently Bloom and Hastie,[4] by using a quadrupole mass spectrometer, were able to identify all the gaseous species above molten $PbCl_2 + PbBr_2$ and were able to detect, besides $PbBr_2$ and $PbCl_2$, only the mixed halide $PbClBr$. The correct vapor phase equilibrium is therefore

$$PbCl_2(g) + PbBr_2(g) = 2PbClBr(g)$$

Complex gas equilibria involving mixed and polynuclear halides were investigated by Buchler et al.[5] by mass spectrometry and weight-loss effusion measurements. Rhenium trichloride vapor consists of a single species, the very stable trinuclear Re_3Cl_9. Similar results were obtained with the bromide above which Re_3Br_9 is the only species. In these experiments the parent ions $Re_3X_9^+$ are in much larger concentration than their fragment ions. In the tungsten and molybdenum oxides, on the other hand, an entire series of polynuclear species is found. Thus W_3O_9 is the major species in the vapor of tungsten trioxide, but W_4O_{12} and W_5O_{15} are also formed, and in the $W + WO_2$ system, WO_3, W_2O_6, and W_3O_9 are also present in the gas phase. Various oxyhalide vapor species were also detected by Buchler et al. by the vaporization of rhenium trichloride, including $ReOCl_4$ and ReO_3Cl from oxychloride contaminants in the samples. The mixed gaseous halide Re_3ClBr_8 was also inferred above mixtures of $ReCl_3$ and $ReBr_3$.

Other Reactions

Complex equilibria in the gas phase can result from many types of reactions summarized by Brewer.[6] These include disproportionation reactions, such as

$$2TiBr_3(s) = TiBr_4(g) + TiBr_2(s)$$

and

$$Hg_2Cl_2(s) = HgCl_2(g) + Hg(g)$$

as well as vaporization by decomposition, such as

$$BaS(s) = Ba(g) + S(g)$$

7-3 COMPLEX FORMATION ABOVE MOLTEN SALT MIXTURES

Numerous examples occur in the literature of the formation of complexes above molten and solid salt mixtures. These include $KCl \cdot FeCl_2$, $CsCl \cdot FeCl_2$, and $NaCl \cdot AlCl_3$. The apparent partial pressures of $PbCl_2$ and KCl were measured by Barton and Bloom[7] above molten $PbCl_2 + KCl$ mixtures. The results are shown in Fig. 7-1. The method used was to measure total vapor pressure by an absolute (boiling point) method and the vapor composition by transpiration. At 900°C the apparent vapor pressures of $PbCl_2$ show negative deviations from Raoult's law, while those of KCl are far in excess of the Raoult's law values, in conflict with the Duhem-Margules equation, which for this system would take the form

$$\frac{d \ln P_{PbCl_2}}{d \ln x_{PbCl_2}} = \frac{d \ln P_{KCl}}{d \ln x_{KCl}}$$

where x_{PbCl_2} and x_{KCl} are the mole fractions of $PbCl_2$ and KCl, respectively, in the liquid mixture. The most probable explanation of these results is the formation of one or more complexes between $PbCl_2$ and KCl in the vapor phase. The shape of the apparent partial pressure isotherm of KCl shows that the 1:1 compound is the most likely, since from the Gibbs-Duhem relationship, the partial pressure of the equimolar compound would have a maximum value in the vapor in equilibrium with an equimolar mixture of the two component liquids. In the $PbCl_2 + KCl$ system (and in the $CdCl_2 + KCl$ and $CdCl_2 + NaCl$ systems investigated by the same authors) the apparent

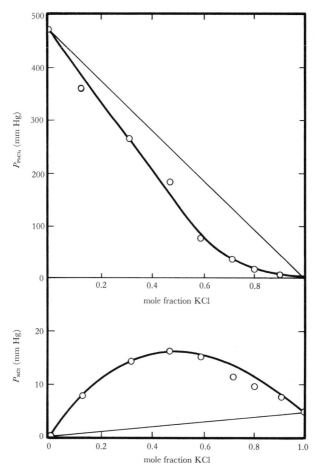

Fig. 7-1. *Apparent partial pressure isotherms for PbCl₂ + KCl system at 900°C versus composition of liquid. (From H. Bloom, Pure Appl. Chem., 7, 389 (1963).)*

partial pressure of alkali halide has a maximum deviation from the Raoult's law ideal values at a melt composition of about 0.5 mole fraction, hence vapor phase compounds are $PbCl_2 \cdot KCl$, and so on.

In a recent study by mass spectrometric measurements on the vapors that effuse from a Knudsen cell containing molten salt mixtures, Bloom and Hastie [4] were able to confirm the presence of complex molecules of the type $AMCl_3$ (A is an alkali metal, M is the divalent metal) above the high temperature solid and molten systems $CdCl_2 + RbCl$, $CdCl_2 + CsCl$, $PbCl_2 + RbCl$, and $PbCl_2 + CsCl$. Table 7-3 gives the observed fragment ions and

Table 7-3 *Observed Complex Ions and Their Molecular Precursors* [a]

Ion	Molecular precursor	Abundance (%) relative to MCl^+	Temperature (°K)
$CsCdCl^+$	$CsCdCl_3$	6	771(s)
Cs_2Cl^+	Cs_2Cl_2	—	771(s)
$CsCdCl^+$	$CsCdCl_3$	—	838(l)
$CsCdCl_2^+$	$CsCdCl_3$	1.9	860(l)
$CsCdCl^+$	$CsCdCl_3$	1.9	860(l)
Cs_2Cl^+	Cs_2Cl_2	—	860(l)
$CsPbCl_2^+$	$CsPbCl_3$	—	913(l)
$CsPbCl^+$	$CsPbCl_3$	—	913(l)
$CsPbCl_2^+$	$CsPbCl_3$	10	790(s)
$CsPbCl^+$	$CsPbCl_3$	—	790(s)
$CsPbCl_2^+$	$CsPbCl_3$	20	785(s)
$RbPbCl_2^+$	$RbPbCl_3$	—	873(l)
$RbCdCl_2^+$	$RbCdCl_3$	—	843(l)
$RbCdCl^+$	$RbCdCl_3$	—	843(l)

[a] Presence of ions and precursors was observed at Compositions 0.50 (± 0.04) Mole Fraction and Ionizing Electron Energies 24–90 eV.

their molecular precursors. Similar results were found for the $PbCl_2$ + KCl system, for which it was found that about 20% $KPbCl_3$ was present at 900°C.

By careful experiments with a sensitive quadrupole mass spectrometer, the same authors were able to identify the parent molecule ions (which were present only in low yield). A summary of many of the various vapor phase complexes obtained by a variety of methods by different authors is given in Table 7-4.

Vapor Phase Complex Formation in the $MgCl_2$ + KCl System

Schrier and Clark [8] measured the vapor pressures of the pure molten salts KCl, $MgCl_2$ and mixtures of KCl and $MgCl_2$ between 900 and 1150°C by boiling point and transpiration methods. Calculation was made for the pure components, by means of Eq. (7-8), of the degree of association at various temperatures, and from these the vapor pressures of KCl monomer, KCl dimer, $MgCl_2$ monomer, and $MgCl_2$ dimer in each pure component salt vapor were calculated on the assumption that only monomer and dimer were in equilibrium. For mixtures of $MgCl_2$ + KCl at 1075°C the total vapor pressures as determined by the absolute (boiling point) method and the apparent vapor pressures as determined by transpiration are shown in Fig. 7-2. The true vapor pressures are given only by the boiling point determi-

Table 7-4   *One-to-One Vapor Compounds over Binary Systems*

Inferred molecule	Temperature (°K)	Method [a]
NaCdCl$_3$, KCdCl$_3$, KPbCl$_3$	1173(l)	Transpiration vapor pressure; m.s.
RbPbCl$_3$, RbCdCl$_3$, CsPbCl$_3$, CsCdCl$_3$	973(l)	Transpiration vapor pressure; m.s.
KMgCl$_3$	1075(l)	Transpiration and boiling point vapor pressure
LiFeCl$_3$, KFeCl$_3$	1123–1273(l)	Transpiration and static vapor pressure
KFeCl$_3$	673–773(s)	M.s. detection of KFeCl$_2$$^+$
LiFeCl$_3$, NaFeCl$_3$, KFeCl$_3$, CsFeCl$_3$, KNiCl$_3$, KCoCl$_3$	1020	Magnetic deflection of molecular beams
CsCoCl$_3$		Electronic absorption spectrum
KFeCl$_3$, KFeBr$_3$		Molecular beam velocity analysis
LiBeF$_3$	900	M.s. detection of LiBeF$_2$$^+$
LiFeCl$_3$	750	M.s. detection of LiFeCl$_2$$^+$
NaZrF$_5$	1167	M.s. detection of NaZrF$_5$$^+$
LiAlF$_4$	1000	M.s. detection of LiAlF$_3$$^+$
NaAlCl$_4$	ca. 430(l)	Vapor pressures
NaAlF$_4$	1000	X-ray and chemical analysis
KLaCl$_4$, KCeCl$_4$, KPrCl$_4$, KNdCl$_4$, KErCl$_4$	1200–1400(l)	Vapor pressure

[a] The m.s. in this column means mass spectrometry.

nations, as this method is completely independent of vapor phase association equilibria; this pressure, and hence the activities of the components, appears to have a minimum at 0.67 mole fraction KCl. This minimum has been correlated with the formation of MgCl$_4^{2-}$ in the liquid phase by Flood and Urnes.[9]   The heat of mixing results of Kleppa and McCarty (Section 4-8) confirm that this is the only complex formed in the liquid.   The apparent total vapor pressure curve in the MgCl$_2$ + KCl system has a quite different shape from the real vapor pressure curve, indicating that there is vapor phase interaction between the two components.

The difference between apparent total vapor pressure and true total vapor pressure is shown as a function of liquid composition in Fig. 7-3.   This difference curve is made up of the combined contributions of (KCl)$_2$, (MgCl$_2$)$_2$, and a complex (MgCl$_2$)$_x$·(KCl)$_y$, but as it comes to a maximum at the composition of liquid given by MgCl$_2$·KCl, the Gibbs-Duhem equation indicates that the formula of the complex is likely to be KMgCl$_3$.

Schrier and Clark were able to confirm the composition of the vapor phase compound by an analytical procedure.   As a model it was postulated

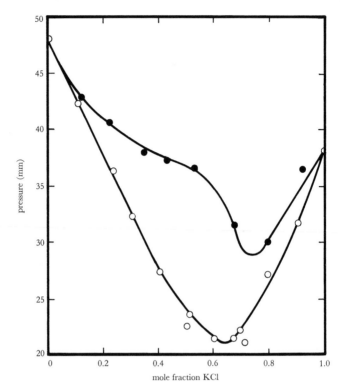

Fig. 7-2. ●, *Apparent total vapor pressure and* ○, *actual total vapor pressure of MgCl₂ + KCl mixtures versus composition of liquid at 1075°C (from Schrier and Clark* [8]).

that the only vapor species present in the mixed vapor are KCl, (KCl)₂, MgCl₂, (MgCl₂)₂, and KMgCl₃. By combination of the transpiration and the boiling point data, the various contributions by each constituent to total vapor pressure were computed and are shown in Fig. 7-4. In this case, for ease of solution, the calculated vapor pressures were restricted to MgCl₂, (MgCl₂)₂, and KMgCl₃ when MgCl₂ is present in excess, and KCl, (KCl)₂, and KMgCl₃ when KCl is in excess. It is clear from Fig. 7-4 that the formula KMgCl₃ is valid for the vapor phase compound as originally assumed, since the calculated pressure of this compound is a maximum at about 0.5 mole fraction. The need to carry out a repetition of the calculations for other postulated complexes therefore does not arise.

One of the most important theoretical applications of the determination of complexes between components in the vapor is to enable activities, as calculated by apparent vapor pressure measurements, to be corrected for

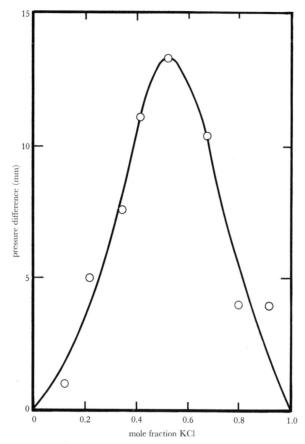

Fig. 7-3. *Difference between apparent total vapor pressure and actual total vapor pressure for the $MgCl_2$ + KCl system at 1075°C versus composition of liquid (from Schrier and Clark [8]).*

such complexes. In many cases the apparent vapor pressures of the components of the mixtures, although slightly higher than the true values because of vapor complexes, give substantially the correct activity values owing to the small proportion of these complexes. In the $MgCl_2$ + KCl system, however, the correction of apparent partial pressures of $MgCl_2$ and KCl for calculation of activity by means of Eq. (4-4) is essential owing to the large proportion of $KMgCl_3$ formed in the vapor, particularly around 0.5 mole fraction composition of liquid. From the practical point of view, the formation of vapor phase complexes accounts for the loss by this process of component salts that would be thought to be nonvolatile.

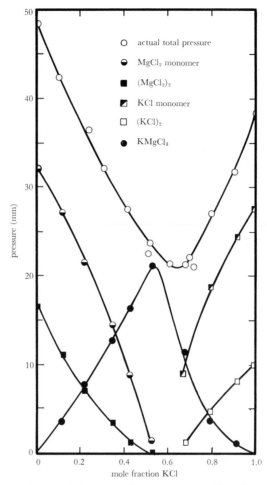

Fig. 7-4. *Calculated partial pressures of the components and actual observed total pressure for the MgCl₂ + KCl system at 1075°C. (From Schrier and Clark.⁸)*

SUGGESTED READING

Bauer, S. H., and Porter, R. F., in *Molten Salt Chemistry* (M. Blander, ed.), p. 607, Interscience, New York, 1964.

REFERENCES

1. Brewer, L., and Brackett, E., *Chem. Rev.*, **61**, 425 (1961).
2. Salstrom, E. J., and Hildebrand, J. H., *J. Am. Chem. Soc.*, **52**, 4641 (1930).

3. Greiner, B., and Jellinek, K., *Z. Phys. Chem.* (*Leipzig*), **165,** 97 (1933).
4. Bloom, H., and Hastie, J. W., *Aust. J. Chem.*, **19,** 1003 (1966); *J. Phys. Chem.*, **71,** in press (1967).
5. Buchler, A., Blackburn, P. E., and Stauffer, J. L., *J. Phys. Chem.*, **70,** 685 (1966).
6. Brewer, L., *Natl. Nucl. Energy Ser. Div. IV*, **19b,** 193 (1950).
7. Barton, J. L., and Bloom, H., *Trans. Faraday Soc.*, **55,** 1792 (1959); *J. Phys. Chem.*, **63,** 1785 (1959).
8. Schrier, E. E., and Clark, H. M., *J. Phys. Chem.*, **67,** 1259 (1963).
9. Flood, H., and Urnes, S., *Z. Elektrochem.*, **59,** 834 (1955).

8

Metal–Molten Salt Solutions

In the absence of a displacement reaction, metals are soluble only in their own molten salts. When an added foreign metal is able to displace a metal from its molten salt, solubility may also take place, but the system then becomes one of the metal dissolved in a mixture of its own salt with the salt of the foreign metal. Quite a large number of binary metal + metal–salt systems have been studied in detail, mostly by phase equilibrium investigations.

8-1 SOLUTION OF ALKALI METALS IN THEIR MOLTEN HALIDES

Alkali metals have strong solubility in their molten halides. They have mainly been investigated by Bredig and co-workers.[1] For cesium systems there is complete miscibility in all proportions above the liquidus, while for potassium, sodium, and lithium systems two immiscible liquids, one essentially a solution of metal in molten salt and the other a solution of molten salt in metal, can result over large ranges of temperature and composition. Rubidium systems are intermediate. At suitably high temperatures for every molten alkali metal + halide system there is miscibility in all proportions.

142

The phase diagrams of CsCl + Cs (representing a system in which there is only one liquid phase) and KCl + K (a system in which two liquid phases may be in equilibrium) are depicted in Fig. 8-1.   Such diagrams may be obtained by a variety of experimental methods, including conventional determination of freezing point lowering of the salt by the added metal. The most widely used method of investigation of these systems, however, has been to sample the various phases in equilibrium at fixed temperatures and to establish their compositions by analysis.   A lighter liquid can be isolated by decantation at high temperature into the sidearm of a container, while a heavier liquid can be isolated by means of a ball check valve, which can

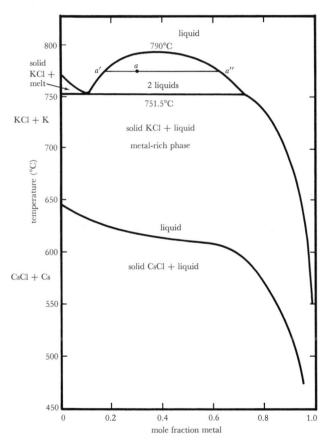

Fig. 8-1. *KCl + K and CsCl + Cs phase diagrams.   (From J. W. Johnson and M. A. Bredig, J. Phys. Chem., **62,** 604 (1958); M. A. Bredig, H. R. Bronstein, and W. T. Smith, J. Am. Chem. Soc., **77,** 1454 (1955).)*

be introduced from a suitably situated side tube. Another method of study makes use of equilibration followed by quenching, bu errors can then occur by occlusion of small droplets of one phase in another. Apart from the determination of phase diagrams, many other physical properties, such as electrical conductance and emf of cells, have been investigated for these systems.

Completely Miscible Systems

Very considerable solubility is observed for cesium in molten cesium halides. Only one liquid phase can be in equilibrium with the solid salt. The phase diagram for this system is depicted in Fig. 8-1. CsCl melts at 645°C, whereas Cs melts at about 30°C; hence the equilibrium will always be between solid salt and liquid metal-containing phase, except near the composition and melting point of the pure metal, where a eutectic between salt and metal is formed. As the solubility of salt in the metal, although considerable at high temperatures, is less than 10^{-7} mole fraction at temperatures approaching the melting point of the pure metal, it is clear that the eutectic composition and melting point will be substantially the same as for the pure metal. Any liquid mixtures obtained by heating a mixture of solids above the liquidus curve will, on cooling, deposit solid CsCl at the liquidus temperature—this will be in equilibrium with a solution containing metal and molten salt whose composition is given by the liquidus line at any particular temperature. The RbBr + Rb system is similar to the cesium halide + cesium systems.

Partially Miscible Liquid Systems

The KCl + K system as depicted in Fig. 8-1 is qualitatively typical of all other alkali halide + alkali metal systems, apart from those already discussed. In this system above 790°C there is complete miscibility of liquid potassium with liquid potassium chloride in all proportions, and only one liquid phase can exist; but below this temperature the equilibrium phases can comprise two immiscible liquids (as well as solid KCl, below 770°C). The limit of coexistence of the two immiscible liquids, 790°C, is the consolute temperature. The area bounded by the solubility curves and the line at 751.5°C is that in which two liquid phases will be in equilibrium. Hence if a mixture of 0.3 mole fraction K and 0.7 mole fraction KCl is heated to, say, 850°C, a single liquid phase will result. If this liquid is cooled to 775°C, it will then consist of two immiscible liquids which are solutions of composition a' and a'' instead of a single liquid a. One liquid will be richer in potassium and the other richer in KCl. The compositions of these conjugate solutions as well as their proportions can be estimated from the phase diagram by drawing a horizontal line at the relevant temperature across the two-phase region.

Other regions of the phase diagram are similar to those discussed under Section 4-3. Thus at low mole fractions of K (<0.11) the cooling of a solution to the liquidus temperature will cause a separation of solid KCl in equilibrium with the melt. Any mixture containing less than about 0.7 mole fraction potassium will, on cooling to 751.5°C, consist of solid KCl in equilibrium with the two conjugate liquid mixtures; hence under these conditions, according to the phase rule, there will be no degree of freedom (at a fixed pressure). The system will therefore remain at the constant temperature until at least one phase has disappeared. The equilibrium line at 751.5°C is known as the monotectic, or monotectic horizontal, and denotes the equilibrium between solid salt and two liquids of different composition. Below the monotectic horizontal there is an area of the phase diagram where the molten mixture is in equilibrium with solid KCl containing very small amounts of metal in solid solution. Outside this area there is a region of complete miscibility of salt and metal. Although the main features of the phase diagrams for all alkali metal systems except Cs halides + Cs and RbBr + Rb are the same, the values of consolute and monotectic temperatures, etc., are of course different for each. The consolute temperatures decrease in the sequence

$$Li > Na > K > Rb$$

and their temperatures range from about 1330° to 800°C for the fluorides. The solubilities of the alkali metals in their molten halides increase in the order

$$Li < Na < K < Rb < Cs$$

Physical Properties of Alkali Halide + Alkali Metal Systems

Molten alkali metal solutions in their molten halides are intensely colored and have very high electrical conductances. Thus the addition of 0.1 mole fraction K to molten KCl at 820°C increases the specific conductance about tenfold. The effect is shown in Fig. 8-4. For K in KI a conductance of about 400 times that of the pure salt has been measured at 0.42 mole fraction K, and the conductance is at that point 99.5% electronic. Metallic sodium also increases the specific conductance by solution in molten sodium halides.

Bronstein and Bredig [2] defined a quantity Λ_M, called the apparent equivalent conductance of the dissolved metal, by the equation

$$\Lambda_M = \frac{\Lambda_{sol} - (1 - f_M)\Lambda_{salt}}{f_M} \tag{8-1}$$

where Λ_{sol}, Λ_{salt} are equivalent conductances of the solution and pure salt, respectively, and f_M is the equivalent fraction of the metal. Λ_M represents the change of conductance caused by the addition of one equivalent of metal to an amount of salt in the solution of given composition held between two electrode plates 1 cm apart. The apparent equivalent conductance of Na and K dissolved in chloride and bromide salts is shown in Fig. 8-2.

The concentration dependence of apparent equivalent conductance of potassium in its molten salts is strikingly different from that of sodium solutions, as shown in Fig. 8-2. While the apparent equivalent conductance of potassium rises rapidly with increase of concentration, that of sodium decreases rapidly but tends to come to a minimum for each system, e.g., at approximately 9 mole % Na in NaBr at 900°C. The metal solubility is

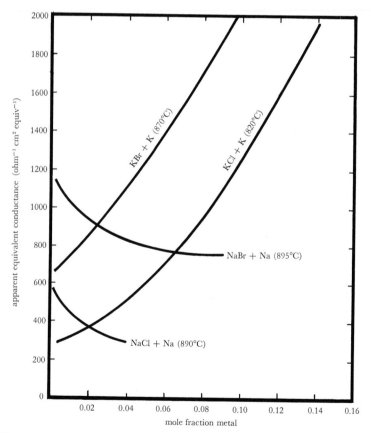

Fig. 8-2. *Apparent equivalent conductance of sodium and potassium metals in their molten chloride and bromide solutions (from Bronstein and Bredig* [2]*).*

considerably less for sodium than for potassium; hence the anticipated increase of conductance at higher concentrations beyond the minimum cannot be physically achieved to any appreciable extent for sodium. At infinite dilution of metal it is clear, from the high conductances, that the electrons in both sodium and potassium solutions are in a state in which they can contribute to the carrying of current. For the pure metals the electron conduction bands confer very much higher conductances, hence the increased conductance of potassium solutions with increasing metal concentration is a result of the progressive approach toward the structure of the pure metal. For the sodium solutions there is clearly a loss of electron mobility and this has been attributed by Bronstein and Bredig to the increased trapping of electrons on increasing the metal concentration from infinite dilution. The reaction

$$2Na^+ + 2e^- \rightleftharpoons Na_2 \tag{8-2}$$

has been suggested as the reason for the decreased equivalent conductance, and its displacement from left to right depends on the stability of Na_2. The same type of equilibrium would not result in as great a loss of electrons in the case of the potassium solutions, owing to the much lower stability of K_2 (as determined in the vapor phase). Sodium solutions would be expected to show an increase of equivalent conductance with increasing metal concentration beyond the minimum along with the progression toward the structure and conductance of the pure metal, but this is frustrated by the comparatively low solubility of sodium in its molten salts. The proportion of diatomic metal species in the alkali metal solutions in their molten halides decreases in the sequence $Li > Na > K > Rb > Cs$.

The activity coefficients of the salts show increasing deviation from ideal mixing values with increasing metal concentration and the plots of $RT \ln \gamma_{salt}$ versus x_M^2 for the KBr, RbBr, and CsI systems are only slightly curved. The approximate linearity of these plots suggests that the metal solutions are regular. The partial excess free energy ($RT \ln \gamma_{salt}$) has been linked by Pitzer [3] with the conversion of the metallic state of bonding of the metal electrons to an ionic type of bonding. Solutions of alkali and alkaline earth metals in their molten salts have been termed "metallic" solutions.

8-2 SOLUTIONS WITH STRONG
SOLUTE–SOLVENT INTERACTION

In contrast to the strong increase of specific conductance on adding alkali metals to their molten salts, "nonmetallic" solutions are formed when a metal such as cadmium is dissolved in its molten halides. Such solutions may have a metallic luster, as for Bi in $BiCl_3$, but their conductances are only slightly different from those of the pure salts—often less for the metal solutions—hence the metallic electrons are strongly bound and not available for conduction.   Subhalides are often formed in such systems, e.g., in the case of Cd in CdCl$_2$ (solubility, 0.152 mole fraction Cd at 600°C), the diamagnetic nature of the solution supports the formation of Cd$_2^{2+}$, or a true solution of Cd atoms.   Freezing point determinations favor the formation of Cd$_2^{2+}$ but the inferred subhalide Cd$_2$Cl$_2$ disproportionates on freezing to give crystalline Cd in solid CdCl$_2$.

The Bismuth Chloride + Bismuth System

In this system the known subhalide, black diamagnetic incongruently melting "BiCl" separates below about 323°C.   The phase diagram for the system is shown in Fig. 8-3, which shows the formation of two immiscible liquids above the temperature of stability of BiCl.   One liquid (L$_2$) consists

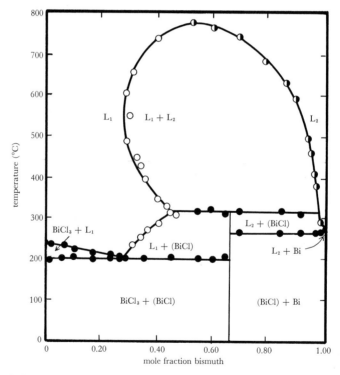

Fig. 8-3.   *Bismuth metal + bismuth trichloride phase diagram:* ◑, *visual;* ○, *decantation;* ●, *thermal analysis.*   *(From S. J. Yosim, A. J. Darnell, W. G. Gehman, and S. W. Mayer, J. Phys. Chem., **63**, 230 (1959).)*

of salt dissolved in the metal and the other (L_1) of metal dissolved in the molten salt. The apparent solubility of Bi in $BiCl_3$ decreases from 0.45 mole fraction at 320°C to 0.28 at 550°C and then increases to the consolute point at 780°C and 0.51 mole fraction Bi. The solubility of salt in the molten metal increases in a steady manner with increase of temperature up to the consolute temperature. The subhalide has been shown by Hershaft and Corbett [4] to be the polymeric species $Bi_{12}Cl_{14}$, hence its formula should be written $BiCl_{1.167}$ rather than $BiCl$.

Solutions of Lanthanide Metals in Their Molten Halides

The rare earth metals dissolve readily in their molten halides with 9%–11% solubility La in $LaCl_3$, approximately 9.5% Ce in $CeCl_3$, and 18.5% Pr in $PrCl_3$. Neodymium is even more soluble in its molten chloride—approximately 30.5%. These systems are somewhat more complex than those already discussed as they occupy an intermediate position between one extreme, that is the alkali metal solutions, which have metallic properties and form no solid subhalide, and the other, that of transition and posttransition metal + molten salt solutions, where metal solubility is generally less and physical properties give no indication of metallic character, in which subhalides exist.

In the lanthanide systems there is evidence for subhalides in many systems, for example, in $Nd + NdCl_3$, the normal divalent salt $NdCl_2$ as well as two intermediate phases separate on cooling the liquid mixtures. There is also evidence for the formation of $PrCl_2$ in solutions of Pr in $PrCl_3$. The formation of subhalides in this class of metal solution differs markedly from similar reactions in transition and posttransition metal solutions in one important respect: the specific electrical conductances of the lanthanide metal solutions in their molten chlorides increase rapidly in many cases with increasing metal concentration, in much the same way as with alkali metal solutions in their molten halides, as shown in Fig. 8-4. The most rapid increase with x_M is found for La in $LaCl_3$ and Ce in $CeCl_3$, hence electronic conductivity is evidenced. There is a smaller electronic effect with Pr in $PrCl_3$. On the other hand, the $Nd + NdCl_3$ system has no component of electronic conductivity and behaves as a mixture of $NdCl_2 + NdCl_3$. For the La, Ce, and Pr systems the electrons from the metal, although contributing appreciably to the conductivity, are not thought to be all simultaneously mobile.

The iodide systems (Fig. 8-4) conduct electronically. With La, Ce, and Pr dissolved in their tri-iodides, apparently stoichiometric di-iodides separate on cooling the molten mixtures, but they have been shown from

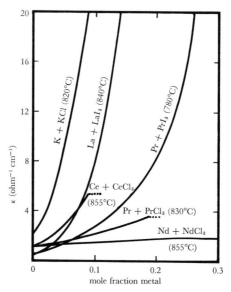

Fig. 8-4. *Specific conductance of molten metals in their molten halides.* $(K + KCl,$
Bronstein and Bredig [2]*; La + LaI$_3$ and Pr + PrI$_3$, A. S. Dworkin, R. A.*
Sallach, H. R. Bronstein, M. A. Bredig, and J. D. Corbett, J. Phys. Chem.,
67, *1145 (1963); Ce + CeCl$_3$, H. R. Bronstein, A. S. Dworkin, and M. A.*
Bredig, J. Phys. Chem., **66**, *44 (1962); Pr + PrCl$_3$ and Nd + NdCl$_3$,*
A. S. Dworkin, H. R. Bronstein, and M. A. Bredig, Disc. Faraday Soc.,
32, *188 (1961); J. Phys. Chem.,* **66**, *1201 (1962).)*

magnetic susceptibility and resistivity measurements to be better described
by the general formula $M^{3+}e^-(I^-)_2$ (Corbett [4]), with a metal-like electron,
rather than MI_2.

The phase diagrams of the lanthanide metal solutions in their molten
halides show that nonstoichiometric solid subhalide phases are formed in
many of the systems. Examples of such compounds are $NdCl_{2.3_7}$, $NdCl_{2.2_7}$,
$PrI_{2.5}$, $CeI_{2.4}$, and $LaI_{2.4_2}$. Some melt congruently, while others melt with
decomposition. These systems have been extensively investigated by Corbett
and co-workers. [4]

8-3 SOLUTIONS OF FOREIGN METALS IN
MOLTEN SALTS (DISPLACEMENT SOLUBILITY)

In the displacement solubility, an equilibrium

$$M_1 + M_{11}X \rightleftharpoons M_1X + M_{11} \qquad (8\text{-}3)$$

is reached and the equilibrium constant K can be measured approximately by the emf of a suitable Jacobi-Daniell cell. For example, for the reaction

$$Cd + PbCl_2 \rightleftharpoons CdCl_2 + Pb \qquad (8\text{-}4)$$

the cell $Cd|CdCl_2\|PbCl_2|Pb$ is investigated. The junction potential is unknown but is generally assumed to be negligible. (Similar values of K are obtained by other methods.) The constant K may be considered to summarize the solubility of metals in salts of a foreign metal and some values are given in Table 8-1.

For many metals the equilibrium $xM + yPbCl_2 \rightleftharpoons xMCl_{2y/x} + yPb$ is displaced almost completely to the right and, as metallic lead is easily separated from a molten salt mixture, this is a convenient method for preparation of anhydrous metal chlorides; for example, at 650°C

$$2U + 3PbCl_2 = 2UCl_3 + 3Pb \qquad (8\text{-}5)$$

Displacement solubility is very important in industrial electrolysis and depends on the electrochemical series of the elements, which will be different in different molten salt solvents and may change with change of temperature. Table 8-2 gives the electrochemical series in various molten salt solvents. The order of metals depends to some extent on the solvent. In $NaBr + AlBr_3$ at 700°C tin will displace silver from $AgBr$, but in $NaI + AlI_3$ at the same temperature silver will displace tin.

Accompanying changes of electrode potentials with variation of temperature, there will be changes of order within the series; for example, for the reaction $2Ag + PbI_2 \rightleftharpoons Pb + 2AgI$, silver will displace lead from molten lead iodide above 685°C, but lead will displace silver from molten silver iodide at lower temperatures.

Table 8-1 *Equilibrium Constants for Displacement Solubility Reactions* [a]

Equilibrium	Temperature (°C)	K
$Na + LiCl \rightleftharpoons NaCl + Li$	900	2.22
$K + NaCl \rightleftharpoons KCl + Na$	900	1.15
$K + NaI \rightleftharpoons KI + Na$	900	58.8
$3Na + AlCl_3 \rightleftharpoons 3NaCl + Al$	825	2×10^9
$Mg + ZnCl_2 \rightleftharpoons MgCl_2 + Zn$	—	6.25×10^4
$Cd + PbCl_2 \rightleftharpoons CdCl_2 + Pb$	600	33

[a] From Delimarskii and Markov.[5]

Table 8-2 *Electrochemical Series of Metals in Molten Salts* [a]

Solvent	Temperature (°C)	Electrochemical series
NaCl + AlCl₃	500	Na, Be, Al, Mn, Tl(I), Zn, Cd, Sn(II), Pb, Co, Ag, Cu(I), Hg(II), Sb(III), Bi, Ni.
NaCl + AlCl₃	700	Na, Al, Mn, Tl(I), Zn, Cd, Pb, Ag, Cu(I), Co, Hg(II), Sb(III), Ni, Bi.
NaBr + AlBr₃	700	Na, Al, Zn, Cd, Pb, Sn(II), Cu(I), Ag, Co, Hg(II), Ni, Sb(III), Bi.
NaI + AlI₃	700	Na, Al, Cd, Ag, Sn(II), Pb, Cu(I), Bi, Hg(II), Co, Ni, Sb.

[a] From Delamarskii and Markov.[5]

8-4 SOLUTIONS OF MOLTEN SALTS WITH NONMETALLIC ELEMENTS

Relatively few investigations have been made of such systems. Rosztoczy and Cubicciotti [6] investigated the KI + I₂, RbI + I₂, and CsI + I₂ systems by thermal analysis and found them to be similar in general behavior. The RbI + I₂ is depicted in Fig. 8-5. The most notable features are the formation of the incongruently melting compound RbI₃ and the formation of a single liquid phase only. The latter is typical of the MI + I₂ systems.

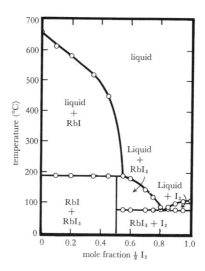

Fig. 8-5. *RbI + I₂ phase diagram (from Rosztoczy and Cubicciotti [6]).*

In the $KI + I_2$ system, no intermediate compound was found, whereas in the $CsI + I_2$ system there are two incongruently melting compounds, CsI_3 and CsI_4.

8-5 SOLUTIONS OF MOLTEN SALTS IN METALS

Figure 8-1 illustrates the solubility of KCl in molten K and CsCl in molten Cs. It is clear that there is considerable solubility and this is typical of alkali halide + alkali metal systems. Bismuth halides are also strongly soluble in molten bismuth, as shown in Fig. 8-3, and $HgCl_2$ is quite soluble in Hg. Many other systems have much smaller solubility of molten salt in molten metal, e.g., 0.30 mole % $PbCl_2$ in molten Pb at 735°C and 1.02% at 1009°C.

REFERENCES

1. Bredig, M. A., in *Molten Salt Chemistry* (M. Blander, ed.), p. 367, Inter-science, New York, 1964.
2. Bronstein, H. R., and Bredig, M. A., *J. Am. Chem. Soc.*, **80,** 2077 (1958).
3. Pitzer, K., *J. Am. Chem. Soc.*, **84,** 2025 (1962).
4. Corbett, J. D., in *Fused Salts* (B. R. Sundheim, ed.), p. 341, McGraw-Hill, New York, 1964; Hershaft, A., and Corbett, J. D., *Inorg. Chem.*, **2,** 979 (1963).
5. Markov, B. F., and Delimarskii, Yu.K., in *Electrochemistry of Fused Salts*, Sigma Press, Washington, D. C., 1961.
6. Rosztoczy, F. E., and Cubicciotti, D., *J. Phys. Chem.*, **69,** 1687 (1965).

9

Some Applications of Molten
Salt Chemistry

Uses for molten salts as reaction media have recently expanded greatly
in many directions and research at present in progress will undoubtedly
uncover many more.

9-1 CHEMICAL REACTIONS IN MOLTEN SALTS

Chemical reactions in molten salts have been investigated extensively
by Sundermeyer [1] and others. They consist of several types: (a) those
utilizing the molten salt as a reacting species; (b) those that are carried out
in the molten salt as (unconsumed) solvent; and (c) those for which the melt
acts as a catalyst.

The Solubility of Refractory Materials in Molten Salts

Reactions between melts and common refractory materials, e.g., Al_2O_3,
SiO_2, and Pt may be classified as corrosion reactions and are the cause of
some of the difficulties of physical measurements on molten salt systems.

154

These can be regarded as acid–base reactions with a basic oxide dissolving in acidic melts, or acidic SiO_2, etc., dissolving in a basic molten salt, e.g., Na_2CO_3. Corundum (Al_2O_3) dissolves rapidly in $Na_2CO_3 + B_2O_3$ molten mixtures and the rate increases considerably with increasing concentration of B_2O_3. The Al_2O_3 is dissolved as an alumino-borate complex containing from 3 to 5 boron atoms per Al.

When alkali hydroxides are melted in the presence of oxygen and water vapor, peroxides are formed; these solutions will dissolve all known refractories except ThO_2. Such melts are useful for difficult oxidations; for example, on adding MnO_2, the reactions

$$2MnO_2 + 6KOH + \tfrac{1}{2}O_2 = 2K_3MnO_4 + 3H_2O \qquad (9\text{-}1)$$

and

$$2K_3MnO_4 + \tfrac{1}{2}O_2 + H_2O = 2K_2MnO_4 + 2KOH \qquad (9\text{-}2)$$

take place. K_3MnO_4 is formed between 240° and 300°C in the presence of hydroxide, while K_2MnO_4 is formed in the presence of peroxide. With ozone as the oxidizing agent Np(VI) oxide can be isolated in an alkali nitrate melt containing Np salts in lower oxidation states.

Reciprocal Reactions

Reactions involving reciprocal salt pairs are capable of being used for industrial preparations. Figure 9-1 shows the activity of $PbCl_2$ in mixtures of $PbSO_4 + NaCl$ as determined by vapor pressure measurements. For

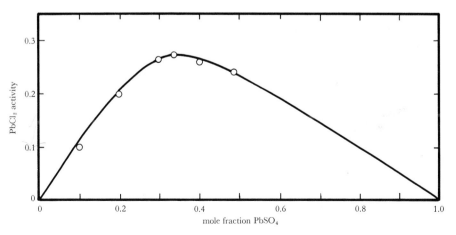

Fig. 9-1. *Activity of $PbCl_2$ in molten $PbSO_4 + NaCl$ mixtures at 730°C. (From H. Bloom and B. J. Welch, Disc. Faraday Soc., **32**, 115 (1962).)*

this system the reaction

$$PbSO_4 + 2NaCl \rightleftharpoons PbCl_2 + Na_2SO_4$$

may lead to the preparation of $PbCl_2$ by condensation of the $PbCl_2$ vapor that leaves the molten mixture. Other reactions are commercially exploitable and required products may be recovered by vaporization, fractional crystallization, or by separation as an immiscible phase.

Halogenation Reactions

Such reactions have considerable industrial importance. Several processes are used for dissolving aluminum-based nuclear reactor fuel elements and recovering the uranium as UF_6. The solvent is typically $KF + ZrF_4 + AlF_3$ at 575°C and uranium is dissolved as UF_4 by reaction with HF. To recover the uranium, fluorine is passed through the melt to convert the UF_4 to volatile UF_6. ClF_3 can also be used as the fluorinating reagent. Zr and more than 99% of the fission products remain in the melt.

The preparation of volatile chlorides from oxides by chlorinating at 800°C under reducing conditions leads, for example, to the preparation of BCl_3 from a eutectic mixture of Na, Ca, Ba chlorides in which B_2O_3 (10%) has been dissolved.

$$B_2O_3 + 3C + 3Cl_2 \rightarrow 2BCl_3 + 3CO \qquad (9\text{-}3)$$

Silicon tetrachloride can similarly be prepared.

Tantalum pentachloride has been prepared by Parker and Wilson [2] by carbochlorination of a tantalite ore containing 44% Ta with 60%–70% recovery. The tantalites were first reduced with carbon to the crude metals and/or metal carbides; these were then reacted with chlorine to give chlorides. The overall reactions were

$$Fe(TaO_3)_2 + 6C + 6\tfrac{1}{2}Cl_2 \rightarrow 2TaCl_5 + FeCl_3 + 6CO \qquad (9\text{-}4)$$

$$Fe(NbO_3)_2 + 6C + 6\tfrac{1}{2}Cl_2 \rightarrow 2NbCl_5 + FeCl_3 + 6CO \qquad (9\text{-}5)$$

$$Mn(TaO_3)_2 + 6C + 6Cl_2 \rightarrow 2TaCl_5 + MnCl_2 + 6CO \qquad (9\text{-}6)$$

The molten mixture of chlorides was fractionally distilled, giving high purity $TaCl_5$, which was used to prepare pure tantalum by high temperature reduction with hydrogen.

Hydrogenation

The synthesis of boron and silicon hydrides can readily be carried out in molten salt solvents such as the $LiCl + KCl$ eutectic at 400°C. The silicon or boron halide vapors are passed through the solvent containing lithium hydride and the reaction, e.g.,

$$4LiH + SiCl_4 \rightarrow SiH_4 + 4LiCl \qquad (9\text{-}7)$$

takes place. If an electrolysis is carried out in the same melt using a cathode over which hydrogen is continuously bubbled, LiH is continuously regenerated.

An interesting preparation of B_2H_6 has been described by Barton and Nicholls,[3] who obtained pure boron monoxide by reaction of boron carbide with TiO_2 or ZrO_2 *in vacuo* at 1600°C by the reaction, e.g.,

$$5TiO_2 + 4B_4C = 5TiB_2 + 3B_2O_2 + 4CO$$

The boron monoxide was collected on a water-cooled copper cold finger placed close to the reaction mixture in the hot zone. When a stream of hydrogen was passed over the solid B_2O_2 at 1200°C, the volatile products collected in a series of cold traps at -196°C were found to consist mainly of B_2H_6 (yield 3%–20% based on B_2O_2).

Molten Salts as Catalysts

Melts are excellent solvents for chlorination reactions, e.g., of acetylene. Chlorine and acetylene together with CCl_4 as a diluent react in a NaCl + $AlCl_3$ + $FeCl_3$ melt at about 200°C to give a mixture of ethylene chloride, tetrachloroethylene, and carbon tetrachloride. Vinyl chloride can be obtained by several routes; for example, by reaction of ethylene, hydrogen chloride, and oxygen in a ratio of 2:2:1 using a $CuCl_2$ + KCl solvent, vinyl chloride is obtained in 61% yield. Catalytic elimination and addition reactions proceed also in molten salt solvents; for example, vinyl chloride can be prepared by thermal dehydrohalogenation of 1,1- and 1,2-dichloro-ethanes using a $ZnCl_2$ + KCl solvent. Yields approach 100% in such reactions and contact times are very small.

9-2 KINETIC STUDIES OF ACID–BASE PROPERTIES IN MOLTEN SALT SYSTEMS

These have been extensively studied by Duke and co-workers.[4]

Examples of Lewis acids (electron pair acceptors) and Lewis bases (electron pair donors) in the class of molten salts are shown in Table 9-1.

Table 9-1 *Molten Salt Lewis Acids and Bases*

Acids	Bases	Neutralization products
SiO_2	O^{2-} [a]	SiO_3^{2-} or SiO_4^{4-}
Al_2O_3	O^{2-} [a]	AlO_2^- or AlO_3^{3-}
B_2O_3	O^{2-} [a]	BO_2^- or BO_3^{3-}
PO_3^-	O^{2-} [a]	PO_4^{3-}
$S_2O_7^{2-}$	O^{2-} [a]	SO_4^{2-}
BeF_2	F^- [b]	BeF_4^{2-}
AlF_3	F^- [b]	AlF_6^{3-} and AlF_4^-
ZrF_4	F^- [b]	ZrF_5^-
$Cr_2O_7^-$	O^{2-} [c]	CrO_4^{2-}

[a] From MO, $M(OH)_2$, MCO_3, MSO_4, etc.
[b] From NaF, etc.
[c] From $NaNO_3$.

The Nitryl or Nitronium Ion (NO_2^+) (Duke [4])

If a suitable Lewis acid is added to a molten nitrate, the equilibrium

$$A^{n+} + NO_3^- \rightleftharpoons AO^{(n-2)+} + NO_2^+ \qquad (9\text{-}8)$$

is assumed to take place as in aqueous solutions and is followed by the reaction

$$NO_2^+ + NO_3^- \rightarrow 2NO_2 + O \qquad (9\text{-}9)$$

The oxygen atoms subsequently combine to form O_2. The reaction between NO_2^+ and NO_3^- is slow and can be followed quantitatively. It is of first order with respect to NO_2^+. The concentration of NO_2^+ can be followed if it is assumed to be proportional to the concentration of Lewis acid A^{n+}; this is reasonable, as the equilibrium reaction (9-8) proceeds only a little from left to right.

If the Lewis acid $S_2O_7^{2-}$ is added to the $NaNO_3 + KNO_3$ eutectic, the reactions that ensue are

$$S_2O_7^{2-} + NO_3^- \rightleftharpoons NO_2^+ + 2SO_4^{2-} \qquad (9\text{-}10)$$

followed by (9-9), which causes a decrease in the total acid concentration in the mixture according to the rate equation

$$\frac{-dA_T}{dt} = k[NO_2^+] \qquad (9\text{-}11)$$

where A_T = total acid concentration, t = time, and k = rate constant; $[NO_3^-]$ is taken as constant as it is part of the solvent. Since

$$A_T = [S_2O_7^{2-}] + [NO_2^+] \tag{9-12}$$

and

$$\frac{[NO_2^+][SO_4^{2-}]^2}{[S_2O_7^{2-}]} = K \tag{9-13}$$

the rate of disappearance of total acidity A_T can be expressed, from (9-11), (9-12), and (9-13), as

$$-\frac{dA_T}{dt} = \frac{kKA_T}{K + [SO_4^{2-}]^2} \tag{9-14}$$

The total acidity is followed easily by reacting weighed samples of the quenched reaction mixture in water and titrating the H^+ formed by the hydrolysis of $S_2O_7^{2-}$ and NO_2^+ (each produces one hydrogen ion). The sulfate concentration can be varied from run to run and is kept much higher than the original $[S_2O_7^{2-}]$; thus the only variable on the right-hand side of (9-14) is A_T in a given run, and a plot of $\ln A_T$ against t gives a straight line of slope

$$\frac{-kK}{K + [SO_4^{2-}]^2}$$

If the negative slopes of these logarithmic plots are designated as k', then

$$k' = \frac{kK}{K + [SO_4^{2-}]^2} \tag{9-15}$$

and

$$\frac{1}{k'} = \frac{1}{k} + \frac{[SO_4^{2-}]^2}{kK} \tag{9-16}$$

This leads to an evaluation of both rate constant and equilibrium constant for reactions of the type (9-10), as a plot of $1/k'$ against $[SO_4^{2-}]^2$ gives a straight line of slope $1/kK$ and an intercept on the $1/k'$ axis of $1/k$. The straight line has an intercept on the $[SO_4^{2-}]^2$ axis of $-K$. If the acid is $S_2O_7^{2-}$, the values of K are small but significant in the range 235°–275°C ($K = 0.026$–0.038). If $Cr_2O_7^{2-}$ is the acid, however, K becomes of the order of 10^{-12} and the reaction with nitrate ion proceeds to a negligible extent unless Pb^{2+} or Ba^{2+} is added to precipitate chromate formed by

$$Cr_2O_7^{2-} + NO_3^- \rightleftharpoons NO_2^+ + 2CrO_4^{2-} \tag{9-17}$$

Although the NO_2^+ species conveniently explains the kinetics of the above reactions, its presence in molten salt systems has not been unambiguously confirmed. (See the results of a polarographic investigation by Topol *et al.*[5])

9-3 THE PRODUCTION OF ALUMINUM BY ELECTROLYSIS

The Hall-Héroult electrowinning process utilizes molten cryolite, Na_3AlF_6, as a solvent for Al_2O_3 at temperatures a little less than 1000°C. Carbon electrodes are used, the cathode being the lining on the inside of the steel-fabricated cell. The anodes are generally "prebaked" carbon rods of cross section up to 60 in. prepared from petroleum pitch and coke. Electric currents used are as high as 130,000 amp with a potential drop per cell of approximately 5 volts. During the working of the cell the cathode is covered by a layer of molten aluminum, which has a higher density than the molten salt electrolyte, containing 2–5 weight percent Al_2O_3 together with CaF_2 and other fluorides such as LiF. The addition of CaF_2 improves the efficiency of the process, but as molten CaF_2 has a higher density than cryolite and aluminum, the practical concentration limit is reached when the density of the bath increases to the point when aluminum globules begin to float. The practical limits of current efficiency are 75%–90%. The decomposition voltage for the electrolyte is theoretically only about 1.2 volts, hence the additional electric power above applied voltages of 1.2 is used for keeping the bath molten and is dissipated as heat. Energy is also lost by secondary electrode reactions, e.g., reoxidation of Al at the anode by CO_2. Electrolysis is continued until the "anode effect" is observed, when Al_2O_3 concentration falls to about 2%. The anode effect, which results in a sudden rise of potential drop per cell to 30 or more volts, is due to the adhesion to the carbon anodes of a gaseous envelope that hinders electrical contact between anode and melt and leads to the passage of current across it in the form of many tiny arcs and sparks. The onset of the anode effect is the signal to add more Al_2O_3 in a batch-worked cell.

The mechanism of the electroreduction of Al is not completely understood. The most significant feature of the $AlF_3 + NaF$ phase diagram shown in Fig. 4-6 is the broad liquidus peak of the congruently melting compound $AlF_3 \cdot 3NaF$ corresponding to cryolite. Such broadening of the liquidus boundary indicates partial decomposition of the solid compound on melting, and it has been postulated that AlF_6^{3-} is partially decomposed to AlF_4^- (and $2F^-$). $NaAlF_4$ has been found by X-ray examination of the rapidly condensed vapors above molten cryolite and is formed as a congruently melting compound in the $AlF_3 + NaF$ phase diagram (Fig. 4-6). Apart from Na^+, F^-, AlF_6^{3-}, and AlF_4^-, molten cryolite is assumed to contain ions arising from sodium fluoride dimers NaF_2^-.

Transference studies on molten cryolite containing dissolved Al_2O_3

show that almost all the current is transported to the cathode by Na^+, and a very small proportion of the current is transported to the anode by complex ions containing Al and F. Migration of Al^{3+} to the cathode is negligible, but the primary cathode product is thought to be aluminum. Co-deposition of sodium, which takes place when the concentration of Al-containing species is low, is due to sufficient shift in the Nernst potential to permit Na^+ to discharge. Although the exact nature of the aluminum oxyfluoride complex is not known, Grjotheim et al.[6] have suggested a variety of ions, including $Al_2O_2F_4^{2-}$, $AlOF_3^{2-}$, and $AlOF_5^{4-}$. At the anode, the oxygen liberated is believed to form CO_2 as the primary anode product by consumption of the anode carbon, but secondary reaction between CO_2 and C produces an appreciable amount of CO (10%–50%). During the anode effect the composition of the anode gas consists of CF_4 and CO (with no CO_2).

9-4   MOLTEN SALT FUEL CELLS

Fuel cells are those in which fuel is continuously fed into a galvanic cell and converted, by chemical reaction with air or oxygen, directly into electrical energy. Such cells are not limited in their efficiency by the Carnot cycle and may, in principle, be 100% efficient. High temperature fuel cells originate from the early work of Baur (1900–1940) employing molten carbonates as the electrolyte (usually an equimolar Na_2CO_3 + K_2CO_3 mixture). H_2 or CO was used as the fuel and air as the oxidant in the temperature range 800°–900°C. Other fuel gases (e.g., H_2 and Cl_2) can be used in other molten salts.

A more modern cell, developed by Ketelaar and Broers,[7] is shown in Fig. 9-2. This cell is operated in the temperature range 500°–900°C. H_2 (with addition of H_2O) or CO (with added CO_2 and H_2O) or CH_4 (with H_2O) are the fuel gases used. Both anode and cathode are of fine metal powder, made by reduction of metal oxide with H_2 or CO, with metal gauze backing, which aids electrical contact. For the cathode, silver powder with silver gauze backing is used and for the anode, Pt, Ni, Cu, Cr, and Mn powders with Pt, Ni, or Cu metal gauze backings have been used. The electrolyte is a mixture of Li, Na, K, carbonates impregnated in a porous magnesia matrix. Asbestos and mica ring gaskets are used as separators and electrical connections are made to stainless steel plates, which prevent deformation of the gauze electrodes during operation. Current densities up to 150 ma cm^{-2} can be drawn at temperatures as low as 500°C with no electrode polarization. The purpose of the CO_2 is to prevent concentration polarization.

The cell reactions in molten salt fuel cells are not completely known.

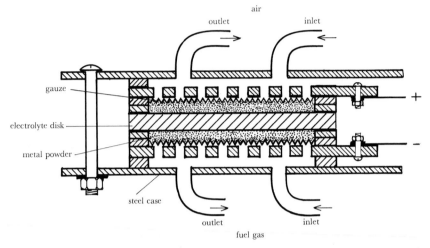

Fig. 9-2. *The Ketelaar-Broers high temperature fuel cell (from Ketelaar and Broers [7]).*

Steam is required for operation of the Ketelaar-Broers cell and primary reactions may be

$$CH_4 + H_2O = CO + 3H_2 \qquad (9\text{-}18)$$
$$CO + H_2O = CO_2 + H_2 \qquad (9\text{-}19)$$

The main anode reaction would be the electrochemical oxidation of H_2 by the reaction

$$CO_3^{2-} + H_2 = H_2O + CO_2 + 2e^- \qquad (9\text{-}20)$$

At the cathode the reaction is

$$CO_2 + \frac{1}{2}O_2 + 2e^- = CO_3^{2-} \qquad (9\text{-}21)$$

The reason for the addition of CO_2 to the fuel gas is, therefore, to maintain a constant composition of CO_3^{2-} in the electrolyte by replacing CO_3^{2-} used in the anode reaction. The overall cell reaction is

$$H_2(g) + \frac{1}{2}O_2(g) = H_2O(g) \qquad (9\text{-}22)$$

and the standard emf of the cell is related to the standard free energy change ΔG^0, of the cell reaction by the relation

$$\mathcal{E}^0 = \frac{-\Delta G^0}{2\mathfrak{F}} \qquad (9\text{-}23)$$

where $\mathfrak{F}$ is the faraday.   The cell emf, i.e., the open-circuit voltage, can then be deduced from the van't Hoff (or reaction) isotherm

$$-\Delta G^0 = RT \ln K_p \qquad (9\text{-}24)$$

where K_p is the equilibrium constant for the fuel gas reaction at temperature T (°K).
Thus

$$z\mathfrak{F}\mathcal{E}^0 = RT \ln K_p \qquad (9\text{-}25)$$

where z electrons are involved in the reaction ($z = 2$ for the Ketelaar-Broers fuel cell), and

$$\mathcal{E}^0 = \frac{RT}{z\mathfrak{F}} \ln K_p \qquad (9\text{-}26)$$

Values of K_p are very high (commonly 10^{10}–10^{12}) for reactions suitable for such cells; that is, $\mathcal{E}^0$ is of the order of 1 volt.   In actual working, however, the value of the cell voltage varies between wide limits, depending on fuel gas composition, current density ($\mathcal{E}$ decreases with increasing current density), temperature, and electrode materials.   In the case of the Ketelaar-Broers fuel cell, voltage varies between 1.2 and 0.3 volt.

Other electrode reactions are also possible in molten salt fuel cells; e.g., at the cathode

$$\frac{1}{2} O_2 + 2e^- = O^{2-} \qquad (9\text{-}27)$$

O^{2-} would be present in the carbonate as a result of the small tendency of the CO_3^{2-} to dissociate.

$$CO_3^{2-} = CO_2 + O^{2-} \qquad (9\text{-}28)$$

CO fuel gas could be anodically oxidized by the reaction

$$CO + O^{2-} = CO_2 + 2e^- \qquad (9\text{-}29)$$

The overall cell reaction would then be

$$CO + \frac{1}{2} O_2 = CO_2 \qquad (9\text{-}30)$$

The Lithium-Chlorine Battery

Several types of battery to produce large currents in a small volume have been developed, including the lithium-chlorine battery described by Swinkels.[8]   This operates at 650°C using molten LiCl electrolyte, the reactions being

$$Li(l) + \frac{1}{2} Cl_2(g) \underset{\text{charge}}{\overset{\text{discharge}}{\rightleftharpoons}} LiCl(l) \qquad (9\text{-}31)$$

The open-circuit voltage is 3.467 volts and the theoretical energy capacity for the reactants is 990 watt hour lb^{-1}. The lithium electrode consists of a BeO tube dipping into molten LiCl electrolyte with a layer of molten Li metal inside floating on the surface of the electrolyte. A stainless steel rod makes electrical contact with the Li anode. The chlorine electrode consists of a porous carbon or graphite plug screwed onto a dense graphite feed tube, which also acts as a current lead. Chlorine is fed into the porous plug. Molten LiCl does not wet graphite; hence there is no penetration of the electrolyte into the pores of the cathode.

9-5 ELECTROANALYTICAL METHODS

Polarography

The investigation of current-voltage curves with a dropping mercury electrode is known as *polarography*, but if a solid microelectrode is used, the same measurement is usually called *voltammetry*. In molten salt investigations both methods have been used and are usually referred to simply as polarography.

In molten salts the techniques used are similar to those in aqueous solutions. Electron transfer reactions are fast and the rate-controlling step is more often the diffusion of ionic species to and from the electrode. The method has important applications for analysis in molten salts as in aqueous solutions. Reference electrodes are based on those used for aqueous solutions, e.g., $Hg|Hg_2Cl_2|KCl + KNO_3 + NaNO_3 + LiNO_3(l)$, and supporting electrolytes are molten mixtures of alkali salts, such as nitrates or a eutectic (e.g., $LiCl + KCl$).

Nachtrieb and Steinberg [9] used the dropping mercury electrode in the low melting $LiNO_3 + KNO_3 + NaNO_3$ mixture against a calomel reference electrode with 0.005 mole fraction KCl added. A span of -0.1 to -1.1 volts against the reference was obtained, and there were well-defined waves for the reduction of Pb(II), Ni(II), Zn(II), and Mn(II). The Ilkovic equation applied, as in aqueous solution.

Laitinen and co-workers [10] have broadened the application of polarographic techniques to include the use of other types of reference electrode, for example, $Pt|Pt(II)$ with molten $KCl + LiCl$ as supporting electrolyte and solid cylindrical or flush platinum, tungsten, and graphite microelectrodes. The reduction of a wide variety of ions, including Cd(II), Bi(III), Cr(II), Cr(III), Cu(I), Cu(II), In(III), Ga(III), Sn(II), Hg(II), Al(III), etc., was investigated. Another major group of investigations has been carried out by Delimarskii and co-workers.[11] Some data are listed in Table 9-2.

Table 9-2 *Polarographic Data in NaCl + KCl*
at 660°C [a, b]

Salt	Concentration (mole liter^{-1} × 10^{-3})	$-\mathcal{E}_{1/2}$ (volt)
CuCl	0.4	0.83
	0.8	0.81
	1.2	0.69
	1.6	0.70
AgCl	0.2	0.85
	0.4	0.81
	0.6	0.75
	0.8	0.76
NiCl$_2$	0.3	0.54
	0.5	0.55
	0.7	0.57
	0.9	0.57
	1.1	0.57
TlCl	0.4	1.39
	0.6	1.30
	0.8	1.32

[a] From Delimarskii and Kuzmovich.[11]
[b] At 660°C $2.303RT/\mathcal{F} = 0.194$.

Chronopotentiometry

The measurement of the time interval between application of a constant current pulse across metal electrodes in an unstirred electrolyte solution and the point at which complete concentration polarization ensues, is known as *chronopotentiometry* (voltammetry at constant current). This interval of time is known as the *transition time*, which is a function of concentration of substance electrolyzed. Chronopotentiometry is one of the most accurate analytical methods for molten salts (accuracy 2%–4%) and the simple electrode systems used in this method give it a considerable advantage over voltammetry for ease of operation. Furthermore, the experimental variables can be suitably controlled so as to enable the measurement of diffusion coefficients of solute ions. This allows the study of complex formation and solubility phenomena.

The fundamental equation for a single diffusing species of uniform initial concentration C was deduced by Delahay and Mamantov [12] as

$$\tau^{1/2} = \frac{z\mathcal{F}\pi^{1/2}D^{1/2}C}{2i_0} \tag{9-32}$$

where τ is the transition time, i_0 is the constant current density in electrolysis,

π has its usual meaning, D is the diffusion coefficient of the ion in square centimeters per second, and z is the number of electrons involved in the reduction (or oxidation) of the diffusing ion.

In the testing of chronopotentiometry as an analytical tool in a sulfate eutectic melt for the determination of $Cu(I)$, Liu [13] used four platinum foil indicator electrodes with areas from 2.2 to 0.3 cm² and current densities ranging from 1 to 4 ma cm⁻². Reproducible transition times up to 7 sec were obtained for all four electrodes. Both the anodic process

$$Cu(I) \rightarrow Cu(II) + e^- \qquad (9\text{-}33)$$

and the cathodic process

$$Cu(I) + e^- \rightarrow Cu(0) \qquad (9\text{-}34)$$

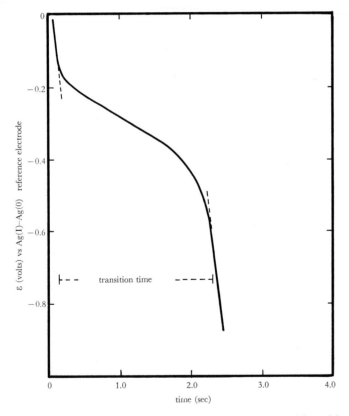

Fig. 9-3. *Cathodic chronopotentiogram. Potential against Ag(I)–Ag(0) reference electrode for reduction of Cu(I) (concentration 5.79 × 10⁻³ molal) to Cu(0) (from Liu [13]).*

were examined.   The platinum indicator electrode was cleaned by electro-
lyzing against a counter electrode, also of platinum, before each measurement of transition time.   An electrolysis at a selected constant current density was then started between indicator and counter electrodes while the
potential of the indicator was simultaneously recorded against a silver reference electrode by means of a chart recorder.   The constant current was
turned off immediately after the transition time was observed and then the
indicator electrode was cleaned electrolytically before the determination was
repeated.   Typical chronopotentiograms are shown in Fig. 9-3 for the
cathodic process (reduction of Cu(I) to Cu(0) at the platinum as negative
electrode) and in Fig. 9-4 for the anodic process (oxidation of Cu(I) to
Cu(II) at the platinum as positive electrode).   It can be seen that the

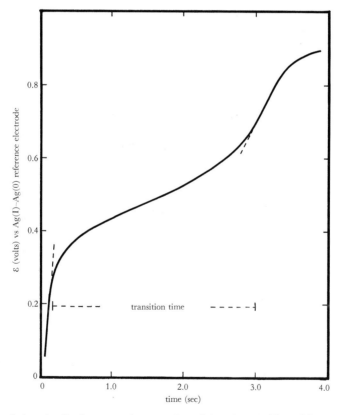

Fig. 9-4.   *Anodic chronopotentiogram.   Potential against $Ag(I)–Ag(0)$ reference electrode for oxidation of $Cu(I)$ (concentration 5.79×10^{-3} molal) to $Cu(II)$
(from Liu* [13]*).*

anodic transition time is considerably longer for the same Cu(I) concentration. The cathodic process is far superior for analytical purposes, as it has much better reproducibility.

Using a chronopotentiometric method, Inman and Bockris [14] were able to deduce equilibrium constants for the successive formation of complex ions of cadmium by measurement of transition times in the absence and presence of halide ion ligands.

9-6 REACTIONS AT EXTREMELY HIGH TEMPERATURES

As temperature increases, e.g., toward 3000°K, the entropy term in the equation

$$\Delta G^0 = \Delta H^0 - T\Delta S^0 \qquad (9\text{-}35)$$

becomes increasingly important and at high enough temperatures far outweighs the heat term in its effect on the equilibrium constant in chemical reactions (Eq. (9-24)).

The study of reactions at temperatures at which the entropy of reaction is all important is difficult to achieve with considerable accuracy, but the recent development of plasma torches has enabled investigations to be carried out to temperatures as high as 50,000°C. Of commercial interest, the preparation of acetylene and fluorocarbons, nitrogen fixation, and the reduction of metal ores have been investigated. A review of the fundamentals of plasma chemistry has been given by Beguin, Kanaan, and Margrave.[15]

REFERENCES

1. Sundermeyer, W., *Angew. Chem. Intern. Ed. Engl.*, **4**, 222 (1965).
2. Parker, S. G., and Wilson, O. W., *Ind. Eng. Chem.*, **4**, 365 (1965).
3. Barton, L., and Nicholls, D., *J. Inorg. Nucl. Chem.*, **28**, 1367 (1966).
4. Duke, F. R., in *Fused Salts* (B. R. Sundheim, ed.), p. 409, McGraw-Hill, New York, 1964.
5. Topol, L. E., Osteryoung, R. A., and Christie, J. H., *J. Phys. Chem.*, **70**, 2857 (1966).
6. Brynestad, J., Grjotheim, K., Grönvold, F., Holm, J. L., and Urnes, S., *Disc. Faraday Soc.*, **32**, 90 (1961).
7. Ketelaar, J. A. A., and Broers, G. H. J., *Ind. Eng. Chem.*, **52**, 303 (1960).
8. Swinkels, D. A. J., *J. Electrochem. Soc.*, **113**, 6, (1966).
9. Nachtrieb, N., and Steinberg, M., *J. Am. Chem. Soc.*, **70**, 2613 (1948); **72**, 3558 (1950).
10. Laitinen, H. A., and Osteryoung, R. A., in *Fused Salts* (B. R. Sundheim, ed.), p. 255, McGraw-Hill, New York, 1964.

11. Delimarskii, Yu. K., and Markov, B. F., in *Electrochemistry of Fused Salts*, Sigma Press, Washington, D.C., 1961; Delimarskii, Yu. K., and Kuzmovich, V., *Zh. Neorgan. Khim.*, **4**, 1213 (1959).
12. Delahay, P., and Mamantov, G., *Anal. Chem.*, **27**, 478 (1955).
13. Liu, C. H., *Anal. Chem.*, **33**, 1477 (1961).
14. Inman, D., and Bockris, J. O'M., *Trans. Faraday Soc.*, **57**, 2308 (1961).
15. Beguin, C. P., Kanaan, A. S., and Margrave, J. L., *Endeavour*, **23**, 55 (1964).

Problems

CHAPTER 4

1. For the galvanic cell

$$Zn(l)|ZnCl_2 \ (x = 0.6) + KCl \ (x = 0.4)|Cl_2(g) \ C \ (graphite)$$

M. F. Lantratov and A. F. Alabyshev, *Zh. Prikl. Khim.*, **27**, 722 (1954) obtained the following results.

t (°C)	emf, ε (volt)	t (°C)	emf, ε (volt)
435	1.6447	490	1.6098
436	1.6435	497	1.6052
440	1.6420	525	1.5870
453	1.6336	545	1.5750
456	1.6325	546	1.5741
461	1.6295	551	1.5695
468	1.6235	561	1.5642
469	1.6230	575	1.5540
477	1.6178	583	1.5502

For this cell, $\varepsilon^0 = 1.5635$ volts at 500°C.

(a) What is the cell reaction?

(b) Plot emf against temperature for the cell and determine the value of ε at 500°C by interpolation.

(c) Calculate the molar free energy, entropy, and enthalpy of the cell reaction at 500°C.

(d) Calculate the activity, activity coefficient, and excess free energy of $ZnCl_2$ at 500°C in the mixture $ZnCl_2$ ($x = 0.6$) + KCl ($x = 0.4$). Can the results be reconciled with the formation of an ideal solution between $ZnCl_2$ and KCl at this temperature and composition?

171

2. For the galvanic cell

$$\text{Pb}(l)|\text{PbBr}_2 \ (x_{\text{PbBr}_2}) + \text{KBr} \ (x_{\text{KBr}})|\text{Br}_2(g), \ \text{C}$$

the values of emf at temperature $t°\text{C}$ (from H. Bloom and M. S. White, to be published) are as follows.

x_{PbBr_2}	emf (volt) at t ($°\text{C}$)
0.801	$1.2981 - (5.391 \times 10^{-4})t$
0.595	$1.3176 - (5.455 \times 10^{-4})t$
0.503	$1.3469 - (5.567 \times 10^{-4})t$
0.395	$1.3616 - (5.262 \times 10^{-4})t$
0.197	$1.3064 - (3.757 \times 10^{-4})t$

(a) Calculate $\bar{G}^E$, $\bar{H}^E$, and $\bar{S}^E$ for PbBr_2 in the various mixtures at 600°C.

(b) Plot activity coefficient of PbBr_2 in the mixtures against mole fraction PbBr_2 (x_{PbBr_2}).

(c) By Gibbs-Duhem integration calculate the activities of KBr and plot them against mole fraction.

(d) Discuss the results.

For pure PbBr_2 at 600°C, the standard heat of formation per mole is -65.74 kcal and its standard entropy of formation is -24.33 cal deg^{-1} mole^{-1}.

3. To determine the activities of CdCl_2 in liquid mixtures of CdCl_2 and KCl at 900°C, J. L. Barton (Ph.D. thesis, Auckland, 1956) measured the partial pressures of CdCl_2 above the molten salt mixtures by transpiration. The results are as follows.

Mole fraction CdCl$_2$ in liquid mixture	Partial pressure of CdCl$_2$ at 900°C (mm Hg)
1.000	437.0
0.890	357.0
0.745	248.0
0.637	167.0
0.541	85.0
0.486	53.0
0.381	22.0
0.340	14.3
0.247	4.9
0.161	1.2
0.117	0.8
0.098	0.7
0.053	0.3
0.000	0.0

Assuming that the vapor consists only of the monomeric species $CdCl_2$ and KCl, calculate (a) the activity (b) the activity coefficient of $CdCl_2$ in the liquid mixtures at 900°C. Discuss the results from the point of view of (1) the information gained on the nature of the liquid mixtures and (2) possible errors due to any assumptions made in the calculations.

4. The results in the table apply to the system $PbCl_2$ + NaCl (S. Sternberg and J. Adorian, *Acad. Rep. Pop. Romîne*, **11**, 315 (1963)).

x_{NaCl}	Temperature of initial solidification (°C)	Eutectic temperature halt (°C)
1.00	801	—
0.90	765	403
0.80	722	403
0.70	670	404
0.60	611	403
0.50	544	404
0.40	476	404
0.30	404	404
0.25	418	405
0.20	438	403
0.15	455	404
0.10	471	403
0.05	483	403
0.00	496	—

For NaCl: $(C_p)_s = 10.98 + 3.90 \times 10^{-3}T$ (°K) cal deg^{-1} mole^{-1}, $(C_p)_l = 16$ cal deg^{-1} mole^{-1}, $\Delta H_{fus} = 6690$ cal mole^{-1}; for $PbCl_2$: $(C_p)_s = 15.88 + 8.35 \times 10^{-3}T$ (°K) cal deg^{-1} mole^{-1}, $(C_p)_l = 27.2$ cal deg^{-1} mole^{-1}, $\Delta H_{fus} = 5650$ cal mole^{-1}.

(a) Calculate the activities of each component of the mixtures at the temperatures of initial crystallization.

(b) Calculate the activities of both components over the whole composition range at 1100°K.

(c) Calculate the excess free energies of each component of the mixture.

(d) Discuss the results in terms of the formation of (1) ideal solutions according to the Temkin model, and (2) regular solutions.

5. From measurements of vapor pressure of $PbCl_2$ above molten mixtures of $PbSO_4$ and NaCl (H. Bloom and B. J. Welch, *Trans. Faraday Soc.*, **57,** 61 (1961)), the thermodynamic activities of $PbCl_2$ in the reciprocal system were determined. The results are as follows.

Weighed-in mole fractions		
$PbSO_4$	NaCl	Activity of $PbCl_2$
0.10	0.90	0.120
0.20	0.80	0.200
0.33	0.67	0.275
0.40	0.60	0.260
0.50	0.50	0.235

(a) Plot a graph of experimental activity of $PbCl_2$ against mole fraction of $PbSO_4$ in the mixture.

(b) Calculate the activities of $PbCl_2$ at various compositions using the Temkin model.

(c) Compare measured and calculated activities and discuss the results.

6. Density and expansivity results for the molten $Li_2O + SiO_2$ system at 1400°C, from the results of J. O'M. Bockris, J. W. Tomlinson, and J. L. White, *Trans. Faraday Soc.*, **52**, 299 (1956), are as follows.

Mole fraction Li_2O	Density (g ml^{-1})	Expansivity $\left(\frac{1}{V}\left(\frac{\partial V}{\partial T}\right)_p\right)$ (deg^{-1} × 10^5)
0.00	2.201	0.0
0.20	2.169	3.4
0.25	2.153	5.5
0.30	2.138	7.2
0.35	2.122	7.7
0.40	2.098	9.0
0.45	2.074	10.4
0.50	2.055	10.7
0.55	2.017	11.5
0.60	1.980	12.6
0.65	1.955	13.2
1.00	1.540	—

(a) Calculate molar volume at 1400°C for each composition and plot molar volume against mole fraction Li_2O.

(b) Estimate partial molar volumes of SiO_2 and Li_2O in the mixtures from 0 to 0.65 mole fraction Li_2O by the method of intercepts and plot against mole fraction Li_2O.

(c) Calculate the molar expansibility $\partial V/\partial T$. (Assume it is zero between 0 and 0.20 mole fraction Li_2O.) Plot this against mole fraction Li_2O.

(d) How do the results fit in with the theory of molten oxide mixtures in Section 2-6?

7. The following are surface tension–temperature relationships for the molten $PbCl_2 + RbCl$ system (from J. L. Dahl and F. R. Duke, *J. Phys. Chem.*, **62**, 1498 (1958), and V. Semenchenko and L. Shikhobalova, *J. Phys. Chem.*, (*USSR*), **6**, 707 (1947)).

Mole fraction RbCl	Surface tension at t (°C) σ (dyne cm^{-1})
0.000	$192.1 - 0.110t$
0.198	$172.6 - 0.103t$
0.319	$165.2 - 0.103t$
0.509	$154.8 - 0.090t$
0.550	$154.2 - 0.090t$
0.578	$159.4 - 0.100t$
0.725	$159.8 - 0.097t$
1.000	$157.1 - 0.083t$

(a) Construct an isotherm of σ versus mole fraction RbCl at 625°C (assume all mixtures are liquid at this temperature).

(b) Calculate the value of σ at 625°C for the equimolar mixture from Guggenheim's equation (4-79) and compare the value with the experimental one. (In this equation, the Boltzmann constant $k = 1.380 \times 10^{-16}$ erg deg^{-1} molecule^{-1}, and the average area per molecule in the surface plane a' can be taken from the molar volume measurements—cf. N. K. Boardman, F. Dorman, and E. Heymann, *Trans. Faraday Soc.*, **51**, 277 (1955)—as

$$a' = \frac{1}{2}\left(\frac{M_A}{Nd_A}\right)^{2/3} + \frac{1}{2}\left(\frac{M_B}{Nd_B}\right)^{2/3}$$

where M is molecular weight, d the density of a particular component, and N the Avogadro number (i.e., 6.023×10^{23} molecules mole^{-1}). At 625°C, $d_{PbCl_2} = 4.762$ and $d_{RbCl} = 2.326$ g ml^{-1}.)

(c) Calculate the surface heat content of each mixture $H^{s/a}$ and plot these values against mole fraction RbCl. Calculate $(\Delta H^{s/a})_{mix}$ from Eq. (4-81) and plot this against mole fraction RbCl.

(d) Discuss the results.

CHAPTER 5

1. The following are results for the specific conductance κ and density d of molten lithium chloride from the measurements of E. R. Van Artsdalen and I. S. Yaffe, *J. Phys. Chem.*, **59**, 118 (1955).

t (°C) [a]	κ(ohm^{-1} cm^{-1})
623	5.692
634	5.826
644	5.892
668	6.008
691	6.118
712	6.225
741	6.370
760	6.463
783	6.540

[a] $d = 1.766 - 0.433 \times 10^{-3}\, t$ g ml^{-1}.

(a) Plot κ against t°C.

(b) From the interpolated values of κ at 630°, 650°, 700°, 750°, and 780°C, together with values of density calculated at these temperatures, calculate equivalent conductance Λ at each of these temperatures.

(c) Plot $\log_{10} \kappa$ against $1/T$°K and from the slope of the line calculate E_κ.

(d) Plot $\log_{10} \Lambda$ against $1/T$°K and from the slope of the line calculate $\Delta H^{\ddagger}$ (i.e., E_Λ).

(e) From the values of E_κ and E_Λ calculate the volume coefficient of expansion (or expansivity) α for molten LiCl. Compare the value of α calculated in this way with that obtainable from the equation for density of LiCl as a function of temperature. (Use Eq. (4-65) for this calculation.)

2. The following are specific conductance and viscosity data, from the results of B. S. Harrap and E. Heymann, *Trans. Faraday Soc.*, **51**, 259 (1955), for the molten salt system $PbCl_2 + AgCl$.

Conductance (ohm^{-1} cm^{-1}) and viscosity (cP)

	Mole fraction AgCl									
	0.000	0.174	0.197	0.380	0.402	0.598	0.608	0.802	0.862	1.000
$\kappa_{450°C}$			1.318		1.560	1.946			2.882	3.700
$\eta_{450°C}$				4.58			3.62	2.93		2.33
$\kappa_{500°C}$	1.430		1.594		1.816	2.196			3.112	3.902
$\eta_{500°C}$	4.56	4.13		3.47			2.95	2.47		2.08
$\kappa_{600°C}$	1.920		2.072		2.266	2.606			3.464	4.212
$\eta_{600°C}$	2.75	2.59		2.30			2.12	1.84		1.66
$\kappa_{700°C}$	2.334		2.508		2.680	2.956			3.732	4.458
$\eta_{700°C}$	1.87	1.99		1.84			1.76	1.65		1.40

(a) Plot the 600°C isotherms of κ versus mole fraction AgCl and η versus mole fraction AgCl.

(b) Calculate the activation energies for conductance E_κ and viscosity E_η, respectively, and plot them against mole fraction AgCl.

(c) The following are densities for the $PbCl_2$ + AgCl system at 600°C from the results of N. K. Boardman, F. H. Dorman, and E. Heymann, *J. Phys. Chem.*, **53**, 375 (1949).

Mole fraction AgCl	0	0.194	0.291	0.389	0.466	0.574	0.797	1.000
Density (g ml^{-1})		4.802	4.790	4.782	4.778	4.775	4.764	4.739	4.698

Plot density against mole fraction of AgCl and use the curve to interpolate for densities at different compositions when required. Calculate the equivalent conductance Λ for the $PbCl_2$ + AgCl system at 600°C and (1) plot Λ against mole fraction AgCl; (2) plot Λ against equivalent fraction AgCl.

(d) Discuss the results.

CHAPTER 6

1. The following refractive index–temperature relationships were determined by H. Bloom and B. M. Peryer, *Aust. J. Chem.*, **18**, 777 (1965) for the $CdCl_2$ + KCl system.

$CdCl_2$ + KCl system [a]

Mole fraction KCl	a	$10^5 b$
0.000	1.696	10
0.114	1.668	13
0.203	1.633	19
0.300	1.607	14
0.360	1.581	20
0.413	1.562	18
0.505	1.534	15
0.598	1.500	14
0.701	1.468	12
0.784	1.448	17
0.811	1.447	16
0.901	1.417	13
1.000	1.397	12

[a] Refractive index $n = a - b(t - 700)$; t = temperature in degrees centigrade.

(a) Calculate molar refractivities of the above pure salts and mixtures at 800°C.

(b) Compare the 800°C molar refractivity isotherm with that at 700°C (Fig. 6-3).

(c) What deductions can you make from the results regarding (1) applicability of the additivity of molar refractivity for this system and (2) the effect of temperature on deviations from additivity?

Molar volumes [M/d in Eq. (6-1) and $(x_1M_1 + x_2M_2)/d$ in Eq. (6-4)] can be obtained from the density results of N. K. Boardman, F. H. Dorman, and E. Heymann, *J. Phys. Chem.*, **53**, 375 (1949) as follows.

Densities of $CdCl_2$ + KCl system [a]

Mole fraction KCl	a	$b \times 10^3$
0.000	3.366	0.84
0.169	3.049	0.96
0.408	2.608	0.95
0.600	2.299	0.82
0.752	2.063	0.72
1.000	1.628	0.60

[a] In this case $d = a - b(t - 600)$ g ml^{-1}.

Plot the molar volume isotherm at 800°C and interpolate.

CHAPTER 7

1. The absolute vapor pressure of molten potassium chloride was measured by J. L. Barton and H. Bloom, *J. Phys. Chem.*, **63**, 1785 (1959) by a boiling point method and apparent molecular weight of the vapor by transpiration experiments. Results are as follows.

Temperature (°K)	Pressure (mm)	Apparent molecular weight
1250	11.6	97.1
1333	32.1	96.1
1416	78.9	93.9
1416	78.9	96.8
1416	78.9	95.5
1416	78.9	94.7
1473	138.0	98.7

Assuming an equilibrium in the vapor, $2KCl \rightleftharpoons (KCl)_2$, (a) calculate degree of association at each temperature and hence the equilibrium constant K atm^{-1} at each temperature. (b) Plot log K versus $1/T$ and, from the slope of the best straight line through the points, estimate the heat of dimerization of KCl vapor per mole of dimer.

2. The vapor pressure of pure molten $CdCl_2$ at 650°C is 10.45 mm. In a transpiration experiment (J. W. Hastie, Ph.D. thesis, Hobart, 1966) dry argon at 760 mm pressure was saturated by vapor above an equimolar liquid mixture of $CdCl_2$ and CsCl at 650°C. It was found by analysis that 17.5 liters of argon (measured at STP) deposited 0.1808 g $CdCl_2$ and 0.0225 g CsCl in the condensing tube. The activity of $CdCl_2$ in the equimolar liquid mixture of $CdCl_2$ and CsCl as obtained from emf measurements is 0.0794 at 650°C. At this temperature the vapors above the molten salt mixture may be assumed to contain only the monomeric forms of CsCl and $CdCl_2$, but as the vapor pressure of pure CsCl at the same temperature is 0.126 mm, it will become clear from the above transpiration results that a vapor phase association equilibrium, which may be assumed to be

$$CsCl + CdCl_2 \rightleftharpoons CsCdCl_3$$

is taking place.

(a) Calculate the apparent partial pressures (mm Hg) of $CdCl_2$ and CsCl, respectively, at 650°C.

(b) Calculate the true partial pressure of $CdCl_2$ in the vapor.

(c) Assuming the presence of CsCl, $CdCl_2$, and $CsCdCl_3$ only, calculate the true partial pressures of $CsCdCl_3$ and CsCl.

(d) What conclusions can you draw from the results under (c)?

CHAPTER 8

1. Equilibrium phase compositions at various temperatures from the results of M. A. Bredig and H. R. Bronstein, *J. Phys. Chem.*, **64,** 64 (1960) for the NaCl + Na system are as follows.

	Mole fraction Na ^{a}	Two liquids temperature (°C)	Monotectic temperature (°C)
Salt-rich phase	0.0293	844	
	0.0310	845	
	0.0316	854	
	0.0324	869	
	0.0384	891	
	0.0387	895	
	0.0397	880	
	0.0425	895	
	0.0755	948	
	0.142	1009	796.5
	0.250	1054	795.0
	0.350	1068	—
	0.500	1079	795.5
Metal-rich phase	0.750	1055	794.6
	0.900	950	792.0

^{a} NaCl melts at 801°C and Na at 98°C.

Construct a phase diagram for the NaCl + Na system and label the various areas, etc. Describe what would happen if a mixture containing 0.8 mole fraction Na were cooled slowly from 1200°C to room temperature.

CHAPTER 9

1. Assuming that the only source of loss of current efficiency in the Hall-Héroult process for the electrolytic extraction of aluminum arises from the secondary reoxidation of the metal by the primary anode product, carbon dioxide (which is reduced to carbon monoxide), calculate the current efficiency if the composition of the anode gas is 70 weight percent CO_2 and 30 weight percent CO.

2. A molten salt fuel cell operating at 800°C uses hydrogen as fuel. The cell reaction is

$$H_2(g) + \frac{1}{2} O_2(g) = H_2O(g).$$

The electrolyte is a molten mixture of alkali carbonates. At 800°C the equilibrium constant for the cell reaction is 2.95×10^9 atm$^{-1/2}$ and the equilibrium is established instantaneously. Calculate the standard open-circuit voltage ($\mathcal{E}°$) for the cell.

Index